AS Fast-Track

Biology

Gareth Rowlands

Series consultants **Geoff Black and Stuart Wall**

Page designer **Michelle Cannatella**

Cover designer **Kube Ltd**

The author would like to thank the Welsh Joint Education Committee for permission to reproduce questions from past exam papers. However, the WJEC are not responsible for the suggested answers to the questions. The full responsibility for these is accepted by the author.

Pearson Education Limited
Edinburgh Gate
Harlow
Essex CM20 2JE, England
and Associated Companies throughout the world

ISBN 0 582 43233-2

British Library Cataloguing-in-Publication Data

A catalogue record for this book is available from the British Library.

Set by 3 in Optima and Tekton
Printed by Ashford Colour Press, Gosport, Hants

Contents

Read this first!

TWO WAYS TO USE THIS BOOK...

This book is designed to be used:

Either

- On its own – work through all the exercises for a quick run-through of your subject. This will take you about 24 hours altogether.

or

- As part of the *Revision Express* system:

1 Read through the topic in the *Revision Express A-level Study Guide* (or similar book).

2 Work through the exercises in this book.

3 Go to www.revision-express.com for extra exam questions and model answers.

4 For even more depth and detail, refer back to your textbook or class notes, and visit the web links from www.revision-express.com.

HOW THE BOOK WORKS

The book is divided into two-page revision sessions. To make your revision really effective, study one session at a time.

Have a short break between sessions – that way you'll learn more!

Each session has two parts:

1st page: the first page on each topic contains interactive exercises to nail down the basics. Follow the instructions in the margin and write your answers in the spaces provided.

2nd page: the second page contains exam questions. Sometimes you'll answer the exam question directly, but more often you'll use it as a starting point for in-depth revision exercises. In each case, follow the extra instructions in the margin.

REMEMBER: the answers in the back are for the revision exercises – they are not necessarily model answers to the exam questions themselves. For model answers to a selection of exam questions go to www.revision-express.com.

All the pages are hole-punched, so you can remove them and put them in your folder.

TRACK YOUR PROGRESS

The circles beside each topic heading let you track your progress.

If a topic is hard, fill in one circle. If it's easy, fill in all three. If you've only filled in one or two circles go back to the topic later.

TOPIC HEADING

EXAM BOARDS

You might not need to work through every session in this book. Check that your exam board is listed above the topic heading before you start a session.

(AS) AQA EDEXCEL OCR WJEC

This book covers the most popular topics. For full information about your syllabus, contact the relevant exam board or go to their website.

AQA
(Assessment and Qualifications Alliance)
Publications department, Stag Hill House, Guildford, Surrey GU2 5XJ – www.aqa.org.uk

EDEXCEL
Stuart House, 32 Russell Square, London WC1B 5DN – www.edexcel.org.uk

OCR
(Oxford, Cambridge and Royal Society of Arts)
1 Hills Road, Cambridge CB2 1GG – www.ocr.org.uk

DON'T FORGET

Exam questions have been specially written for this book. Ask your teacher or the exam board for the official sample papers to add to the questions given here.

COMMENTS PLEASE!

However you use this book, we'd welcome your comments. Just go to www.revision-express.com and tell us what you think!

GOOD LUCK!

Carbohydrates and fats

Large molecules are made up of smaller building blocks. Carbohydrates and fats both contain carbon, hydrogen and oxygen but the elements are arranged differently in the molecules. Their properties and roles or functions in the organism differ.

CARBOHYDRATES ○○○

Carbohydrates include monosaccharides (single-sugars), disaccharides (double-sugars) and polysaccharides (many-sugars).

> State whether the carbohydrates are mono-, di- or polysaccharides and give their function, stating if they occur in plants or animals or both.

Carbohydrate	Group	Role	Plant or animal
glucose			
lactose			
cellulose			
glycogen			

WATCH OUT
Make sure you know the difference between a reducing and non-reducing sugar and the appropriate food test.

When two monosaccharides join together to form a disaccharide a molecule of water is released.

> What term is given for this type of reaction and what type of bond is formed between the two molecules?

Polysaccharides have different roles in living organisms.

> Give the role of each polysaccharide and explain how their general structure is suited to their function.

Starch and glycogen.

Cellulose.

DON'T FORGET
In the ring structure form glucose can exist as α or β isomers. Starch is made up of α-glucose units whereas cellulose is made up of β-glucose units.

FATS OR LIPIDS ○○○

A fat is made up of two different smaller molecules:

> Complete the equation.

= triglyceride + water

Fats perform a variety of functions in both plants and animals:

> List the main functions of fats with an example of where they may be found in each case.

Function	Example

DON'T FORGET
One gram of fat yields approximately twice as much energy as one gram of carbohydrate.

Turn the page for some exam questions on this topic ➤

EXAM QUESTION 1 ●●●

The table compares the properties of organic compounds. If the property is a characteristic feature of the compound mark the appropriate box or boxes with a tick (✔).

Have a go at ticking the boxes. Make sure you consider each box carefully. Each row should have one or more boxes ticked.

EXAMINER'S SECRETS
In this type of question one mark is given for each horizontal row that is completely correct. However, don't tick more boxes than is necessary or you will be penalized for this.

Property	Maltose	Sucrose	Starch	Lipid
a source of energy				
a polysaccharide				
produces monosaccharides on complete hydrolysis				
soluble in water				
a reducing sugar				
a main food store in some seeds				

EXAM QUESTION 2 ●●●

(a) Simple carbohydrate molecules can be written as $(CH_2O)n$. What is the name given to carbohydrates in which n is

   (i)   6

   (ii)   5

   (iii) 3

(b) Simple carbohydrates can be combined to form disaccharides and polysaccharides. What else is produced in these reactions?

(c) (i) Name the reagent used to test for the presence of reducing sugars in food.

DON'T FORGET
Practical food tests and their details.

   (ii) Name a sugar which would *not* give a positive test with this reagent.

EXAM QUESTION 3 ●●●

EXAMINER'S SECRETS
You should be able to recognize and use structural formulae, e.g. glucose, amino acid, fatty acid, glycerol.

In living organisms small molecules are often built into large molecules, often with hundreds of small units repeated. The diagram shows the structural formulae of two such small molecules.

Complete the table.

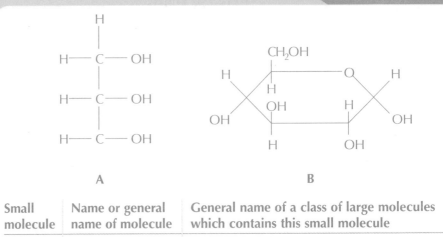

A   B

Small molecule	Name or general name of molecule	General name of a class of large molecules which contains this small molecule
A		
B		

Proteins

There are relatively few carbohydrates and fats but there are a large number of proteins. There are approximately 800 different proteins in a typical bacterium and over 10 000 different proteins in humans! Nevertheless all proteins are polymers constructed from the same set of amino acids.

THE JARGON
A polymer is a large molecule consisting of many identical or similar building blocks (monomers) linked by bonds, just like a train consists of a chain of carriages.

EXAMINER'S SECRETS
You are not expected to recall names of amino acids.

Construct a dipeptide from the diagram. With a coloured pen circle the lower −OH group of diagram A and the lower −H group of diagram B in order to 'remove' the molecule of water formed. Now join together the carbon, to which the −OH was attached, with the nitrogen to which the −H was attached.

Use the information in the table to identify amino acid B and write your answer in the box.

Write an appropriate word alongside each phrase.

STRUCTURE

Amino acids differ according to their side chain or R group.
Diagram A shows the general formula of an amino acid and diagram B shows the formula of one of the 20 amino acids.

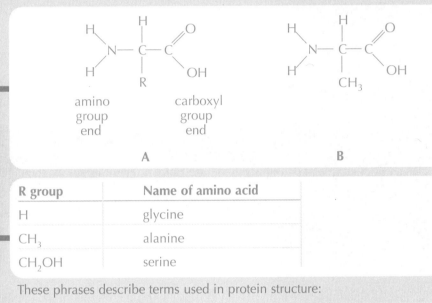

	amino group end	carboxyl group end	
	A		**B**

R group	Name of amino acid	
H	glycine	
CH_3	alanine	
CH_2OH	serine	

These phrases describe terms used in protein structure:

a reaction where a molecule of water is removed	
the type of bond formed when two amino acids join	
a long chain of amino acids	

LEVELS OF PROTEIN STRUCTURE

When a cell synthesizes a polypeptide the chain coils and folds spontaneously, forming a functional protein of specific conformation.
The level of protein structure describes the degree of folding and is determined by the number and types of bonds formed.

WATCH OUT
Take care how you spell *protein*.

Tick the boxes to show which bonds are present at each level of protein structure.

Level of structure	Peptide	Hydrogen	Disulphide	Ionic
primary				
secondary				
tertiary				

CLASSIFICATION

Proteins can be classified according to function which is determined by structure.

Classify the examples of proteins as either globular or fibrous.

insulin	
collagen	
lysozyme (an enzyme)	
keratin	

Turn the page for some exam questions on this topic ➤

EXAM QUESTION 1 ● ● ●

The diagram shows the structural formula of a molecule of a typical amino acid.

> Try this simple question to begin with.

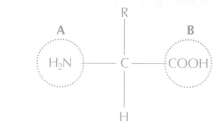

(a) Name the parts of the molecule labelled A and B.

A

B

(b) State what R would represent in the simplest amino acid.

EXAM QUESTION 2 ● ● ●

The diagram shows part of a protein molecule.

> This question requires you to consider the diagram carefully.

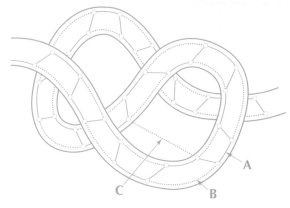

(a) Name the level of protein structure which is shown.

EXAMINER'S SECRETS
Always study carefully the information provided in the question. It is there to help you and you are expected to use the information in your answer.

(b) Suggest a function that such a structure might perform in the body.

(c) Explain what structural feature allows the performance of this function.

LINKS
For more information on enzymes, see page 15.

(d) Name the bonds labelled

A

EXAMINER'S SECRETS
There are several possible correct answers in part (b). Write your explanation as concisely as possible to follow on logically from your answer.

B

(e) Name one other type of bond which might form the bond labelled as C.

Nucleic acids

Nucleic acids store and transmit hereditary information. DNA is unique among molecules in that it provides directions for making copies of itself and also directs RNA synthesis and, through RNA, controls protein synthesis.

CHECK THE NET
You'll learn more about nucleic acids at www.biology.arizona.edu.molecular _bio/problem_sets/nuclei_nucleic _acids_1.htm

> Name the parts of the structure of a typical nucleotide.

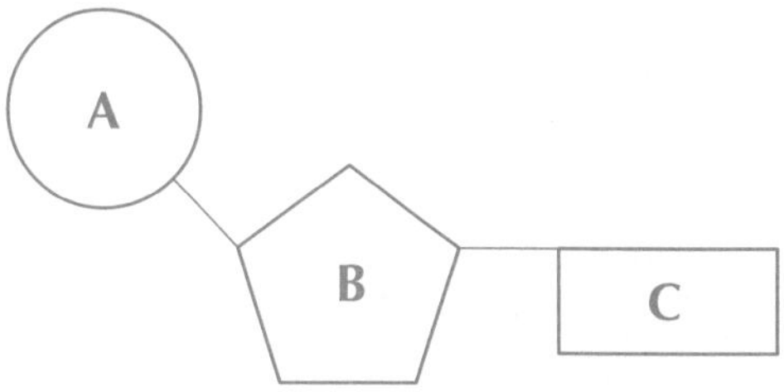

DON'T FORGET
Nucleic acids are polynucleotides with the phosphate group forming a bridge between one sugar molecule and the next by means of a condensation reaction. The bases form the 'rungs' of the 'ladder' and the alternating phosphate and sugar groups form the 'uprights'.

> Complete the table that describes the organic bases.

NUCLEOTIDE STRUCTURE   ○○○

Nucleotides are the sub-units of nucleic acids. They are formed by condensation reactions when three components combine:

A _____

B _____

C _____

Organic bases are divided into two groups.

Name of group	Single or double rings	Names of bases
pyrimidines		
purines		

DEOXYRIBONUCLEIC ACID – DNA   ○○○

Two polynucleotide chains are held together by hydrogen bonds. The greatest number of hydrogen bonds is formed when purines pair with pyrimidines.

> What are the *complementary* base pairs in DNA?

EXAMINER'S SECRETS
Questions are often asked about the *stability* of DNA. You may be expected to explain how this stability is achieved by complementary base pairs.

> List the three types of RNA.

RIBONUCLEIC ACID–RNA   ○○○

DIFFERENCES BETWEEN DNA AND RNA   ○○○

> Complete the table to show some of the differences between DNA and RNA.

WATCH OUT
In RNA adenine pairs with uracil.

	DNA	RNA
single or double chain		
type of sugar		
bases (as abbreviations)		
helix type		
location		

Turn the page for some exam questions on this topic ➤

EXAM QUESTION 1

●●●

The diagram represents the molecular structure of part of a DNA molecule.

Attempt this question on DNA.

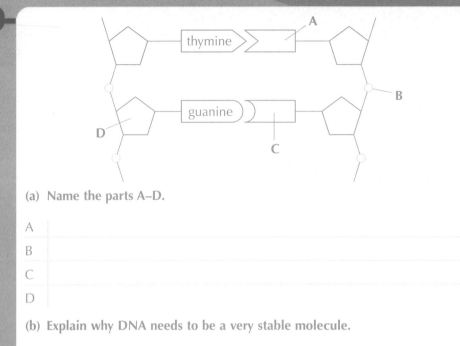

(a) Name the parts A–D.

A

B

C

D

(b) Explain why DNA needs to be a very stable molecule.

(c) Part of a DNA molecule has the following sequence of bases.

Write the sequence of bases of the complementary portion of DNA.

DNA molecule	T	A	T	C	G
complementary DNA					

EXAMINER'S SECRETS
Always show your working. Examiners know that the answer appears on the calculator screen. They also need to know *how* that answer was achieved.

(d) Biochemical analysis of a sample of DNA showed that 30% of the bases were guanine. Calculate the percentage of the bases in the sample which would be adenine. Show how you arrived at your answer.

EXAM QUESTION 2

●●●

The table compares DNA and RNA.

Tick the boxes to show the differences and similarities between DNA and RNA.

	DNA	RNA
contains ribose		
contains uracil		
contains adenine		
double chain		
exists as one form		

Replication

During DNA replication, base pairing enables existing DNA strands to act as templates for new complementary strands.

THE JARGON
Another word for template is blueprint.

Use a coloured pen to complete the diagrams.

HOW REPLICATION TAKES PLACE – SEMI-CONSERVATIVE MODEL ○○○

A parent molecule has two complementary strands of DNA which unwind into two separate strands.

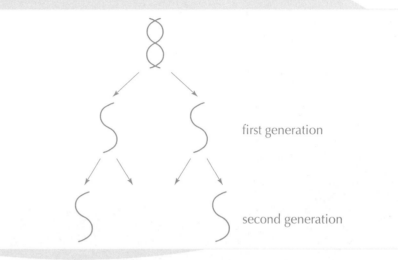

first generation

second generation

EVIDENCE FOR THE THEORY ○○○

Meselson and Stahl devised experiments that tested the two main hypotheses for DNA replication.

1. They cultured the bacterium, *Escherichia coli*, for several generations on a medium containing the heavy isotope of nitrogen, ^{15}N.
2. The bacteria were transferred to a medium containing the lighter, more common form of nitrogen, ^{14}N.
3. They could distinguish DNA of different densities by centrifuging DNA extracted from the bacteria.

THE JARGON
A centrifuge is an instrument that can spin tubes containing liquid suspensions at a very high speed. The denser particles will separate out at a lower point in the tube than the lighter particles.

The following are reasons for experimental steps 1 and 2:
(a) Any new DNA that the bacteria made would be lighter than the 'old' DNA made in the ^{15}N medium.
(b) The bacteria incorporated the ^{15}N into their nucleotides and then into their DNA.

Link the reasons (a) and (b) given for the steps in the experiments with the appropriate experimental step.

Step 1	
Step 2	

The diagram shows the results of the experiments.

Which diagram, A or B, gave the results which provided conclusive evidence for the semi-conservative hypothesis? Tick the box(es) which describe the positions you would expect for the density bands if the experiment was carried out to a second generation.

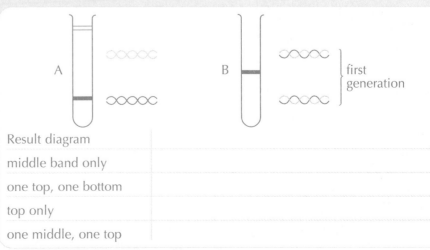

first generation

Result diagram	
middle band only	
one top, one bottom	
top only	
one middle, one top	

Turn the page for some exam questions on this topic ➤

EXAM QUESTION 1

●●●

The polymerase chain reaction is a technique used by biologists to make large amounts of DNA from very small samples. The process is explained in the diagram.

> Make sure you have understood replication before you attempt these questions.

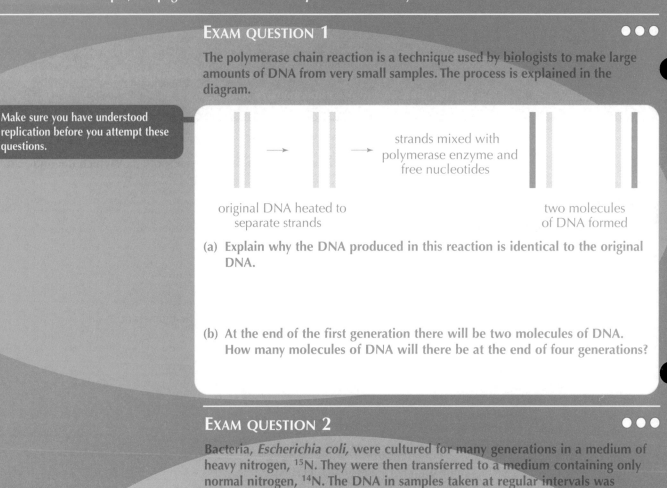

strands mixed with polymerase enzyme and free nucleotides

original DNA heated to separate strands

two molecules of DNA formed

(a) Explain why the DNA produced in this reaction is identical to the original DNA.

(b) At the end of the first generation there will be two molecules of DNA. How many molecules of DNA will there be at the end of four generations?

EXAM QUESTION 2

●●●

Bacteria, *Escherichia coli*, were cultured for many generations in a medium of heavy nitrogen, ^{15}N. They were then transferred to a medium containing only normal nitrogen, ^{14}N. The DNA in samples taken at regular intervals was extracted and centrifuged in a solution of caesium chloride which forms a gradient of increasing density from the top to the bottom of the centrifuge tube. The diagram shows that the DNA forms distinct bands at precise positions where the density of the DNA matches the caesium chloride.

> Read the question carefully then fill in the table. This question needs some thought.

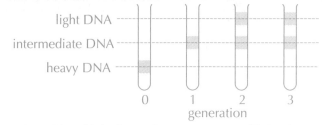

light DNA

intermediate DNA

heavy DNA

| 0 | 1 | 2 | 3 |

generation

(a) Complete the table which shows the percentage of light, intermediate and heavy DNA at the end of generation 0, 1, 2 and 3.

EXAMINER'S SECRETS
This is quite straightforward if you study the diagram carefully.

Generation	Percentage of DNA in each sample		
	Light	Intermediate	Heavy
0	0	0	100
1	0	100	0
2			0
3			0

(b) State the term used to describe the way in which the new molecules of DNA were replicated in this experiment.

(c) Explain why the bacteria were washed thoroughly before they were transferred from the medium containing ^{15}N to one containing ^{14}N as a source of nitrogen.

Protein synthesis

The information content of DNA, the genetic material, is in the form of specific sequences of nucleotides along the DNA strands. A gene is a DNA sequence coding for a specific polypeptide chain.

THE NATURE OF THE GENETIC CODE ○○○

How can only four nucleotides produce 20 different amino acids?
If each nucleotide coded for one amino acid it would be possible to make four amino acids.
What would happen if the code consisted of pairs of nucleotides?

Fill in the boxes in the table, with all the possible permutations of bases in pairs.

	A	T	G	C
A				
T				
G				
C				

Complete the boxes.

Type of code (codon)	Formula	Possible number of amino acids
code in nucleotide pairs	4^2	
code in nucleotide triplets	4^3	

These terms describe the code:

Explain concisely the meaning of the terms.

non-overlapping	
universal	
degenerate	
stop or nonsense	

IF YOU HAVE TIME
Write out a step by step account of protein synthesis using the three stages opposite as headings.

STAGES IN PROTEIN SYNTHESIS ○○○

There are three stages in protein synthesis – transcription, amino acid activation, translation.

Write one word or phrase next to the appropriate definition.

The synthesis of mRNA from DNA code directed by RNA polymerase	
The combination of amino acids with tRNA using energy from ATP	
The synthesis by the ribosome of a polypeptide under the direction of mRNA	

The translation process:

The table lists two amino acids and the base sequences on a DNA strand which code for them in protein synthesis. It will help you arrive at your answer if you first complete the boxes. This is quite tricky!

Amino acid	DNA triplet code	mRNA codon	tRNA anticodon
glycine	CCT		
methionine	TAC		

If a tRNA molecule had an anticodon UAC,
name the amino acid carried by this molecule.

WATCH OUT
In RNA uracil replaces thymine, so A pairs with U.

BIOLOGY

(13)

Turn the page for some exam questions on this topic ➤

EXAM QUESTION 1 ● ● ●

EXAMINER'S SECRETS
In this question only one tick per horizontal row is required.

WATCH OUT
Make sure you explain how you arrived at your answer.

(a) The table shows the functions of DNA, messenger RNA (mRNA) and transfer RNA (tRNA).

Statement	DNA	mRNA	tRNA
site of codon			
site of anticodon			
attaches to ribosome			
translated			
carries amino acid to ribosome			
transcribed but not translated			

(b) The number of bases in a gene coding for a polypeptide is 642. Estimate the number of amino acids in the polypeptide chain.

EXAM QUESTION 2 ● ● ● ●

The diagram shows part of the sequence of events which take place when a protein is synthesized.

EXAMINER'S SECRETS
Be prepared to answer questions on one particular aspect of protein synthesis. Only an essay question can test your knowledge of the whole process.

(a) Name:

the step in protein synthesis shown

the cell organelle where these events take place

feature X

feature Y

feature Z

(b) State the base sequence on molecules L and M.

L

M

(c) Describe fully what happens after the amino acid has been linked in the above process.

Enzymes

Without enzymes, chemical reactions that occur in living organisms would take place very slowly and in an uncontrolled way.

PROPERTIES OF ENZYMES   ○○○

Here are some key terms:

> **Write a concise definition for each term.**

DON'T FORGET
The specificity of an enzyme is attributed to a comparable fit between the shape of its active site and the shape of the substrate. To help understanding, the process is sometimes referred to as a 'lock and key' mechanism.

WATCH OUT
Enzymes are destroyed by high temperatures but work very slowly at 0°C.

catalyst	
activation energy	
active site	
specific	
denature	

Each of the following words or phrases can be applied to one or more of the terms above:
lowers; lock and key; temperature; biological.

> **Write the most appropriate word or phrase beneath each of the key terms above.**

HOW ENZYMES WORK   ○○○

> **Complete the equation.**

Enzyme + substrate →

IF YOU HAVE TIME
Study the 'lock and key' mechanism and consider the 'induced fit' theory.

FACTORS AFFECTING ENZYME ACTION   ○○○

The speed at which an enzyme works can be affected by factors.

> **Apart from inhibition, list four factors that affect enzyme action. Label the horizontal axis of each graph with the appropriate factor.**

DON'T FORGET
Describe enzyme and substrate action in terms of molecular collisions. As temperature increases the kinetic energy of the molecules increases.

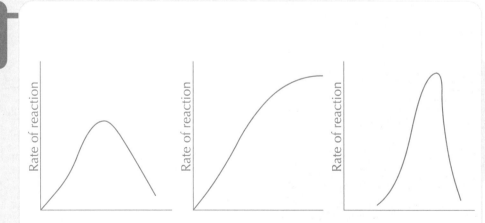

15

BIOLOGY

Turn the page for some exam questions on this topic ➤

EXAM QUESTION 1   ● ● ●

The enzyme sucrase breaks down the disaccharide sucrose to glucose and fructose. Sucrase has no effect on other disaccharides such as lactose or maltose.

With reference to their molecular structure, explain why enzymes such as sucrase can break down some compounds but not others.

Try this question which is about enzyme specificity.

LINKS
For more information on protein structure, see page 7.

EXAMINER'S SECRETS
You could also gain marks by referring to the formation of an enzyme–substrate complex and the 'lock and key'/induced fit hypotheses.

EXAM QUESTION 2   ● ● ●

An enzyme extract from a plant was mixed with substrate and the rate of reaction measured at different temperatures. The results are plotted in the graph below.

Study the graph, then answer the question.

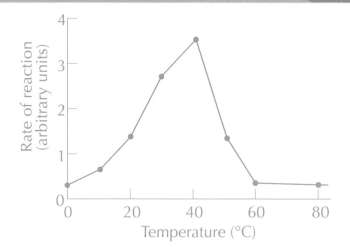

(a) What is the approximate optimum temperature for this enzyme supported by the evidence, and how could this have been more precisely determined?

EXAMINER'S SECRETS
You are expected to deduce from the graph that the experiment has been carried out at 10°C intervals. The optimum *could* be lower or greater than 40°C.

(b) Explain the increase in the rate of reaction between 0°C and 30°C.

DON'T FORGET
Remember to link your practical work to your theory answers.

(c) Explain the decrease in the rate of reaction between 40°C and 60°C.

Enzyme inhibition

Inhibition occurs when enzyme action is slowed down or stopped by another substance. Certain chemicals selectively inhibit the action of specific enzymes, allowing a cell to regulate its metabolic pathways by controlling where and when its various enzymes are active.

COMPETITIVE AND NON-COMPETITIVE INHIBITION ○ ○ ○

These reversible inhibitors are of two types:

> **Describe the inhibitors by answering yes or *no* opposite each statement.**

Features of inhibitor	Competitive	Non-competitive
changes shape of active site		
binds to active site		
similar in structure to substrate		
malonic acid inhibitor		
affected by concentration of substrate		
cyanide inhibitor		

DON'T FORGET
Sketches and graphs will help you understand the differences between the different types of inhibitors.

EXAMINER'S SECRETS
Describe enzyme–substrate reaction in terms of molecular collisions.
With competitive inhibition the greater the substrate concentration in relation to the inhibitor, the greater the *chance* that the substrate will collide with the enzyme.

Competitive and non-competitive inhibitors react differently to an increase in substrate concentration.

The graph shows how the reaction proceeds normally and in the presence of inhibitors.

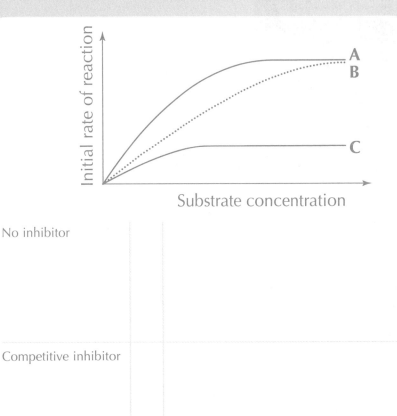

> **In the table label the three lines which appear in the graph. Explain the difference between the shapes of lines A, B and C.**

DON'T FORGET
As the graph shows, the same amount of product is formed with a competitive inhibitor but it takes *longer* to make the products.

DON'T FORGET
Both competitive and non-competitive inhibition are reversible.

No inhibitor	
Competitive inhibitor	
Non-competitive inhibitor	

Turn the page for some exam questions on this topic ➤

17

BIOLOGY

EXAM QUESTION 1 ●●●

EXAMINER'S SECRETS
Note the amount of detail expected in an answer at this level.

(a) Explain what is meant by the term 'competitive enzyme inhibitor'.

(b) A mixture is prepared containing an enzyme, a competitive inhibitor and a small amount of substrate.

   (i) What would be the probable effect on the rate of reaction if more substrate is added?

   (ii) Explain your answer.

EXAM QUESTION 2 ●●●

An enzyme catalyses the reaction between substrates A and B. Molecule C acts as an inhibitor in the reaction.

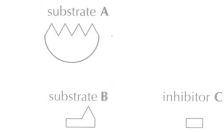
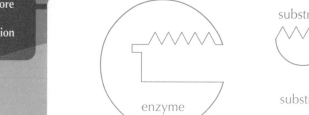

(a) Using the information in the diagram suggest an explanation for this inhibition.

(b) The diagram below shows a reaction sequence with the production of an end product.

SYLLABUS CHECK
Skip part (b) if it's not on your syllabus.

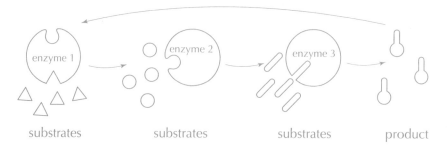

substrates   substrates   substrates   product

When sufficient product has been made how is the reaction stopped?

Enzyme applications

The ability of enzymes to perform as catalysts when isolated from cells has led to their use in industrial processes. Enzymes also have analytical uses in medicine.

COMMERCIAL USES OF ENZYMES

○○○

The table describes some applications of enzymes:

> Complete the table by naming the enzymes involved.

Application	Enzymes used	Uses
'biological' detergents		in pre-soak and main wash to remove protein e.g. blood stains
dairy industry		breaks down lactose to glucose and galactose
food industry		clearing of wines and fruit juices

IMMOBILIZED ENZYMES

○○○

Advantages to using immobilized enzymes instead of 'free' enzymes are as follows:

> List two advantages of immobilized enzymes.

THE JARGON
'Inert 'means 'chemically unreactive'.

THE JARGON
The term 'biosensor' describes the association of a biomolecule, such as an enzyme, with a transducer which produces an electrical signal in response to substrate transformation. The strength of the electrical signal may be measured with a suitable meter.

SYLLABUS CHECK
Skip biosensors if you're doing the Edexcel syllabus.

BIOSENSORS

○○○

The diagram shows a simplified version of a glucose oxidase biosensor used to detect glucose in blood.

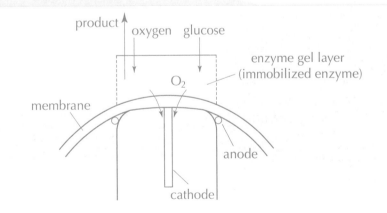

> Sentences 1 to 6 describe how a biosensor is used. But they are in the wrong order! Put them in the correct order starting with sentence number 3.

1. Oxygen is taken up.
2. A digital display shows an accurate concentration of glucose.
3. Blood contains a mixture of different molecules.
4. Enzyme electrode is placed in blood sample.
5. The rate of oxygen uptake is proportional to the glucose concentration.
6. Glucose diffuses into the immobilized enzyme layer.

Turn the page for some exam questions on this topic ➤

EXAM QUESTION 1 ●●●

Enzymes are difficult to recover at the end of an industrial process. However, enzymes are easily reused if they are immobilized. The graph shows the effect of temperature on the maximum rate of reaction with an enzyme in its free state and in its immobilized state.

Have a go at interpreting the graph and diagram in this question.

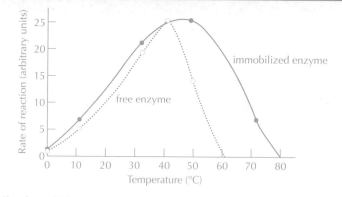

(a) Describe four differences between the effects of temperature on the immobilized and the 'free' enzyme.

(b) Suggest how trapping and holding an enzyme in a framework of cellulose microfibrils, as shown in the simplified diagram below, can explain the differences you have described in (a).

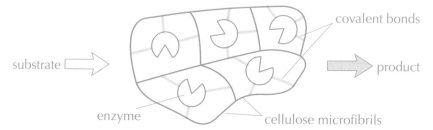

EXAMINER'S SECRETS

An increase in temperature causes an increased movement of molecules. Violent molecular movement results in bonds being broken, resulting in denaturation.

EXAM QUESTION 2 ●●●

(a) State a clinical use of biosensors.

(b) From your knowledge of enzymes, suggest how chemical reactions giving large temperature changes would be unsuitable for measurement by biosensors.

SYLLABUS CHECK

Skip this question if you're doing the Edexcel syllabus.

(c) Suggest two advantages of using a biosensor rather than a chemical test such as Benedict's test to determine the amount of glucose in a test sample.

Cell structure

Every organism is composed of one of two structurally different types of cells: prokaryotic cells or eukaryotic cells. Eukaryotic cells developed from prokaryotic ones with the essential change being the development of membrane-bounded organelles within the cytoplasm of the cell.

CHECK THE NET
You'll find some organelle labelling exercises at wsuonline.weber.edu/course.botany.130/unit1_la.htm

Complete the table to show differences between prokaryotic and eukaryotic cells.

PROKARYOTE AND EUKARYOTE CELLS   ○○○

The table compares prokaryote and eukaryote cells:

Feature	Prokaryotic cells	Eukaryotic cells
nucleus		
chromosomes		
membrane-bounded organelles		
mitosis or meiosis		
ribosomes		

PROKARYOTIC CELLS   ○○○

The diagram shows the structure of a prokaryotic cell e.g. bacterium.

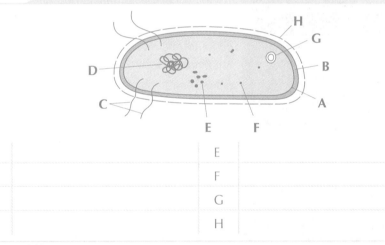

Label parts A to H of the bacterial cell.

A		E	
B		F	
C		G	
D		H	

EUKARYOTIC CELLS   ○○○

The diagram shows the structure of a generalized animal cell with details of organelles.

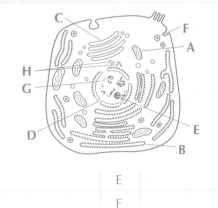

Label parts A to H of the cell.

DON'T FORGET
Make sure you compare plant and animal cells.

EXAMINER'S SECRETS
You should be able to recognize the organelles in cells in electron micrographs.

A		E	
B		F	
C		G	
D		H	

Turn the page for some exam questions on this topic ➤

EXAM QUESTION 1 ●●●

Attempt to compare the two types of cells.

(a) The table lists some of the features of cells. Complete the table by ticking in the appropriate column(s) if a feature is found in eukaryotes, prokaryotes or both.

Feature	Eukaryotes	Prokaryotes
usually less than 10 μm in size		
mitochondria present		
enzymes present		
ribosomes present		
DNA often a continuous loop		
presence of a nuclear membrane		

(b) Name one way in which the plant cell wall differs from that of most prokaryote cells.

EXAM QUESTION 2 ●●●

Tick the boxes to show which structures are present in the three groups of organisms.

WATCH OUT
Some structures are present in more than one group.

(a) The table compares animal, plant and bacterial cells. If the structure is a characteristic feature of the cell mark the appropriate box with a tick.

Structure	Animal	Plant	Bacterium
nuclear membrane			
circular DNA			
endoplasmic reticulum			
mitochondrion			
chloroplast			
cell wall			

(b) In the last 50 years major developments in biological techniques have revolutionized the study of cell organelles. Suggest a technique which has proved vital for the study of:

organelle structure

organelle function

EXAM QUESTION 3 ●●●

Chopped liver tissue was homogenized and the cell organelles present in the homogenate were then separated by centrifugation.

Have a go at interpreting the results of this experimental technique.

(a) Complete the table to show the order in which the mitochondria, nuclei and ribosomes would appear in the pellets at the bottom of the centrifuge tube after each centrifugation.

Speed (g)	Time (minutes)	Organelles in pellet
500–1000	10	
10 000–20 000	20	
100 000	60	

SYLLABUS CHECK
Skip this question if you're doing the Edexcel, OCR or WJEC syllabuses.

(b) What could be measured to show that the mitochondria obtained could still carry out their function?

Cell membrane

The plasma membrane is the boundary which separates the living cell from its non-living surroundings. It exhibits the property of selective permeability, that is, it allows some substances to pass through it more easily than others.

STRUCTURE OF THE MEMBRANE ○○○

The principal biochemical constituents are phospholipid and protein.
The diagram represents a phospholipid molecule.

Name the parts of the molecule labelled A and B and state how they differ in their properties with respect to water.

THE JARGON
Hydrophilic means 'water-liking' or water soluble.

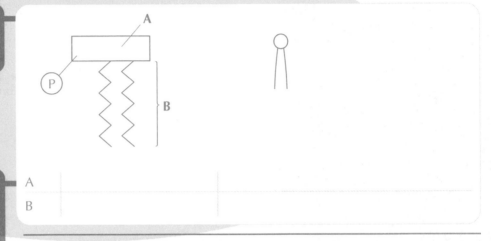

A
B

Use the simplified diagram to show the arrangement of phospholipid molecules in a cell membrane. The sandwich model (1935) proposed that two protein layers are added. Add the protein layers to your diagram.

THE SELECTIVE PERMEABILITY OF THE MEMBRANE ○○○

Substances that move through the membrane do so at different rates. The graph shows the results of an investigation into the passage of various molecules across a cell membrane.

WATCH OUT
This is a difficult concept.
The hydrophobic core of the membrane impedes the transport of ions and polar molecules. These require specific transport proteins to help them across.
Very small molecules that are polar but uncharged e.g. water, can also pass through the membrane rapidly.
Hydrophobic molecules such as oxygen and carbon dioxide which are soluble in lipid can cross the membrane with ease.

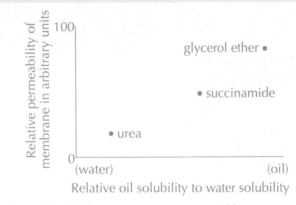

Some of the conclusions of the experiment are correct and some are incorrect. Place a T for true or F for false after each sentence.

1. Urea has low oil solubility, so cannot move quickly.

2. Membrane has low permeability to urea.

3. Membrane has low permeability to glycerol ether.

4. Lipid soluble molecules are more permeable than water soluble molecules.

        1   2   3   4

LINK
Water soluble molecules have to be moved across the membrane by other means. See page 35.

Explain what is meant by the terms 'fluid' and 'mosaic' in this context.

THE FLUID MOSAIC MODEL ○○○

Fluid

Mosaic

Turn the page for some exam questions on this topic ➤

EXAM QUESTION 1

●●●

The diagram shows the fluid mosaic structure of the cell membrane.

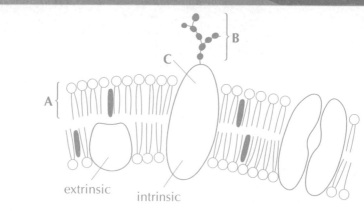

extrinsic   intrinsic

(a) Complete the table by naming the parts of the membrance labelled A, B and C in the diagram and state the function of each.

Structure	Name	Function
A		
B		
C		

(b) Draw an arrow on the diagram to show the path followed by water as it enters the cell.

EXAM QUESTION 2

●●●

Give an account of the general structure of the cell membrane and describe briefly the functions of the membrane.

Write out a plan for this essay question.

EXAMINER'S SECRETS

Although called 'essay questions' it is quite acceptable for you to include diagrams, even when these are not specifically requested. A well annotated diagram can often replace text, save time and can gain just as many marks. This question is a good example where you can do this.

Cell organelles

In addition to the plasma membrane at its outer surface, a eukaryotic cell has extensive and elaborately arranged internal membranes, which partition the cell into compartments. There are also non-membranous structures in the cell.

THE IMPORTANCE OF INTERNAL MEMBRANES ○○○

Internal membranes serve several important functions in cells:

> List three advantages of having membrane-bound organelles.

MEMBRANOUS ORGANELLES ○○○

Membranous organelles carry out a number of different functions.

> Complete the table by naming each structure.

SYLLABUS CHECK
Check your syllabus for the names of the organelles you need to study.

IF YOU HAVE TIME
This topic is ideal for preparing review notes in the form of a flow diagram, placing named organelles in boxes and linking them appropriately with their functions by means of arrows.

Function of structure	Name
controls cell's activities and retains chromosomes	
site of respiration	
site of protein synthesis	
site of photosynthesis	
site of lipid and steroid synthesis	
digests structures or molecules	

NON-MEMBRANOUS ORGANELLES ○○○

Non-membranous organelles also carry out a number of functions.

> This time you complete the functions of these organelles.

DON'T FORGET
Make sure you study the cell wall. It is not an organelle but plays an important role in plant cells.

EXAMINER'S SECRETS
You need to study the various organelles in depth. The nucleus has been included to illustrate this point.

Function of structure	Name
	centriole
	microtubules
	cilia
	microvilli

THE NUCLEUS ○○○

The statements describe parts of the nucleus.

> Identify the parts of the nucleus described.

the outer portion forms part of the endoplasmic reticulum	
coils of DNA bound to proteins in the non-dividing cell	
its function is the assembly of the structural components of ribosomes	
they make it possible for mRNA to reach the ribosomes.	

Turn the page for some exam questions on this topic ➤

EXAM QUESTION 1

● ● ●

The diagram shows part of a mitochondrion.

Label the parts of the diagram, then answer the questions.

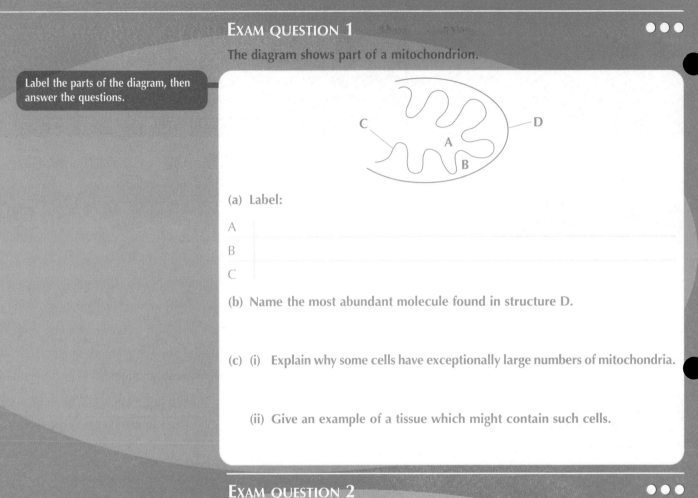

(a) Label:

A _____

B _____

C _____

(b) Name the most abundant molecule found in structure D.

(c) (i) Explain why some cells have exceptionally large numbers of mitochondria.

(ii) Give an example of a tissue which might contain such cells.

EXAM QUESTION 2

● ● ●

The diagram shows the structure of the chloroplast as seen with an electron microscope.

Label the features A to E on the diagram of the organelle.

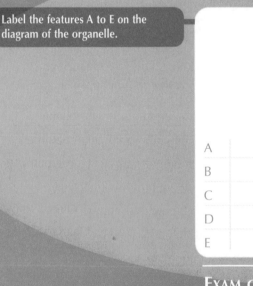

A _____

B _____

C _____

D _____

E _____

EXAM QUESTION 3

● ● ●

The statements describe three membranous organelles.

Tick the boxes to answer this question.

EXAMINER'S SECRETS
You will need to tick more than one box in some horizontal rows.

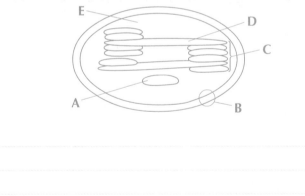

	Rough endoplasmic reticulum	Smooth endoplasmic reticulum	Golgi body
continuous with outer nuclear membrane			
contains abundant ribosomes			
site of lipid synthesis			
main site of peptide bond formation			
produces lysosomes			

Mitosis

Mitosis is the type of cell division which involves the distribution of identical genetic material, DNA, to two daughter cells. The DNA is copied exactly, so that, in humans each new cell receives 46 chromosomes.

CHROMOSOME STRUCTURE ○○○

Each chromosome consists of two threads called chromatids, joined at a point called the centromere. Chromosomes exist in homologous pairs:

> Label A and B in diagram X. Explain what has happened to the chromosomes in diagram Y.

THE JARGON
A homologous pair of chromosomes are the same length, have the centromere in the same position and carry the same genes (though not necessarily the same alleles of these genes) in identical positions.

CHECK THE NET
You'll find a mitosis tutorial at:
www.biology.arizona.edu/cell_bio/tutorials/cell_cycle/main.html

> Fill in the blanks C, D and E.

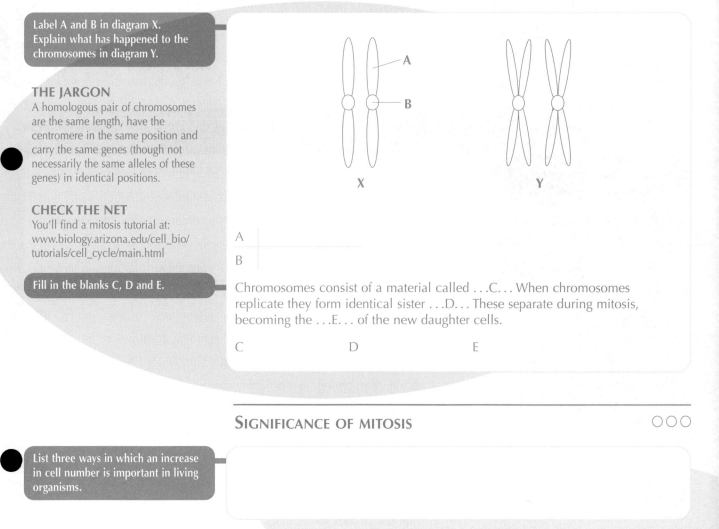

A _____

B _____

Chromosomes consist of a material called ...C... When chromosomes replicate they form identical sister ...D... These separate during mitosis, becoming the ...E... of the new daughter cells.

C _____ D _____ E _____

SIGNIFICANCE OF MITOSIS ○○○

> List three ways in which an increase in cell number is important in living organisms.

STAGES IN MITOSIS ○○○

Dividing cells undergo a regular pattern of events, known as the cell cycle. The following statements describe the **main** events taking place in **animal** cells.

> Write the name of the appropriate stage in the boxes. Be careful, they're not in the correct order.

DON'T FORGET
The cell cycle lasts 8–24 hours in humans and the nuclear division occupies about 10% of this time.

chromosomes attached to equator of spindle	
a period of intense chemical activity which includes the replication of DNA	
chromatids pulled to opposite poles	
cytokinesis occurs	
chromosomes shorten and thicken and spindle forms	

Turn the page for some exam questions on this topic ➤

EXAM QUESTION 1

The diagram shows a three-dimensional view of one of the stages of mitosis in a typical animal cell.

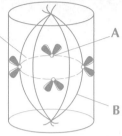

equatorial plane of spindle

A

B

DON'T FORGET
The differences between mitosis cell division in plants and animals.

Name of the stage shown	
Name of structure labelled A	
Function of structure labelled B	

EXAM QUESTION 2

(a) Name a period in mitosis during which DNA replication takes place.

(b) The diagram shows the changes in the DNA content of a cell during one cell cycle.

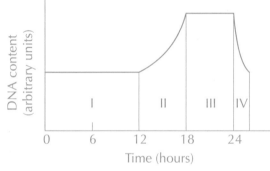

(i) Which part of the diagram, I, II, III or IV, shows when DNA replication is taking place? Explain your answer.

(ii) During which part of the diagram would you expect the chromosomes to have become visible?

(iii) Describe fully what is happening to the cell during the part of the diagram labelled IV.

(iv) What is the name given to this stage in mitosis?

Meiosis

Meiosis separates chromosomes, halving the diploid number, and introduces variation to the haploid products. It occurs in gamete formation.

SIGNIFICANCE OF MEIOSIS   ○○○

Here are some key terms.

Write out the definitions to the terms.

Term	Definition
gamete	
diploid cell	
haploid cell	
fertilization	

SYLLABUS CHECK
OCR, AQA(A), AQA(B) require the principles of meiosis only. Details of the stages of meiosis are *not* required.

IF YOU HAVE TIME
Make cards showing diagrams of the stages of meiosis. Practise putting the cards in the correct order and naming the stages correctly. (Hint: put the names of the stages on the back of the cards.)

In each generation, the doubling of chromosome number that results from fertilization, is offset by the halving of chromosome number that results from meiosis:

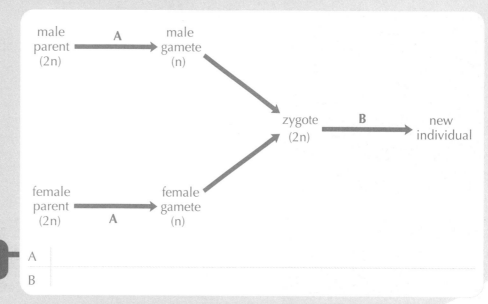

What type of cell division takes place at points A and B?

A _____

B _____

The list shows the diploid number of some plants and animals.

Give the number of chromosomes found in the gametes.

Human	46	
Fruit fly	8	
Onion	16	
Potato	48	

MEIOSIS AND GENETIC VARIETY   ○○○

SYLLABUS CHECK
Skip this unless you are doing the WJEC syllabus.

List three ways in which meiosis promotes genetic variety.

Turn the page for some exam questions on this topic ➤

EXAM QUESTION 1 ● ● ●

The diagram shows four homologous pairs of chromosomes from a cell of the testis of the fruit fly, *Drosophila*.

EXAMINER'S SECRETS
In meiosis there are 16 different possible permutations from four pairs!

DON'T FORGET
In meiosis only one of each homologous pairs of chromosomes goes into each gamete.

(a) If the cell had divided by mitosis, draw the appearance of the chromosomes in circle A, below.

(b) If the cell had divided by meiosis, draw the appearance of the chromosomes in circles B and C, below.

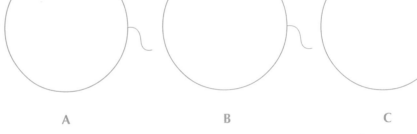

A   B   C

(c) Explain how mitosis maintains genetic stability in an organism.

(d) Explain how 'random fertilization' can bring about variation.

EXAM QUESTION 2 ● ● ●

The table describes four events which take place during cell division.

Tick the appropriate box or boxes to show which of the events apply to mitosis, meiosis I and meiosis II.

SYLLABUS CHECK
Skip this question unless you are doing the WJEC syllabus.

Event	Mitosis	Meiosis I	Meiosis II
chromosomes shorten and thicken			
crossing over between homologous pairs of chromosomes			
double stranded chromosomes move to the poles			
centromeres divide			

Gene technology I

DNA technology has launched a revolution in biotechnology. It has enabled scientists to modify specific genes and move them between organisms as diverse as plants, animals and bacteria.

SYLLABUS CHECK
If you are studying the OCR syllabus very little detail is required.

Draw arrows to link the terms with the correct definitions.

RECOMBINANT DNA TECHNOLOGY ○○○

Here are some key terms and definitions.

1 Recombinant DNA	Enzymes used to synthesize DNA from mRNA in specific cells.
2 Plasmids	Enzymes which cut DNA molecules between specific base sequences.
3 Restriction enzymes	DNA which results from the combination of fragments from two different organisms.
4 DNA ligases	Circular loops of DNA found in bacteria.
5 Reverse transcriptases	Enzymes which join together portions of DNA.

WATCH OUT
You must understand the sequence of this process.

The diagram shows the use of enzymes to make recombinant DNA:

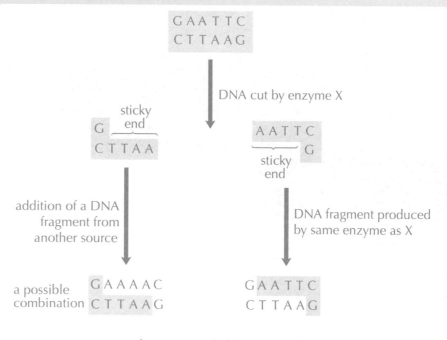

Name the enzymes X and Y involved in the sequence.

Enzyme X	
Enzyme Y	

LINK
For more information see Mitosis on page 27.

A human gene may be cloned in a bacterial plasmid.

The main steps in cloning a human gene are in the wrong order. Place them in the correct order, starting with step 1.

1. Isolate plasmid vector DNA and human DNA.
2. Grow bacteria in culture.
3. Add DNA ligase – to bond covalently.
4. Mix the DNA – they join by base pairing.
5. Cut both DNA isolates with same restriction enzyme.
6. Add recombinant plasmid into bacterium (cloning vector).
7. Tag bacteria using antibiotic resistant sequence.
8. Insert human DNA into plasmids.

Turn the page for some exam questions on this topic ➤

EXAM QUESTION 1 ● ● ●

Biologists in Australia plan to use genetic engineering to produce a gene which they intend to insert into orange trees. They have combined two pieces of DNA to produce a gene which they have called SDLS-2. The parts of this gene are:

DNA sequence that switches on a gene used in seed formation	gene that kills cells

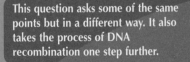
Try this question on genetically engineered oranges.

(a) Explain how biologists could use enzymes:
   (i) to remove a gene from a longer piece of DNA.

   (ii) to join the two pieces together to make the SDLS-2 gene.

(b) Suggest how the SDLS-2 gene might affect the production of the fruit.

(c) Describe the likely advantage of the gene and any possible dangers that might result from growing plants containing this gene.

EXAM QUESTION 2 ● ● ●

The diagram represents part of the process in the production of a crop plant resistant to the broad-spectrum weedkiller, glyphosate.
A represents the gene for glyphosate resistance.

This question asks some of the same points but in a different way. It also takes the process of DNA recombination one step further.

EXAMINER'S SECRETS
Don't be put off by words like 'glyphosate'.
Examiners have to put questions like this into a true context. It should not affect your ability to answer the question.

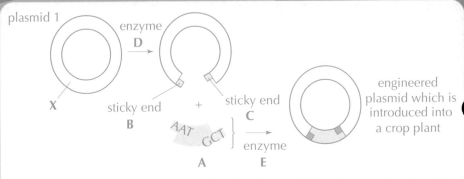

(a) (i) Name the specific biological molecule X which makes up the plasmid.

   (ii) Name the enzyme types represented by D and E.

D

E

   (iii) The diagram shows the sticky ends on A in detail. Enter the base sequence you would expect to find on sticky ends B and C of the plasmid.

B   C

(b) Suggest one advantage to farmers of growing crops resistant to glyphosate.

Gene technology II

DNA technology is in the news almost every day! Usually the topic of the story is a new and promising application to a medical problem. However, DNA technology has also raised questions about possible dangerous consequences of its use.

SYLLABUS CHECK
Skip gene therapy if you're studying the AQA(B) syllabus.

Draw arrows to link the correct descriptions with the appropriate terms.

THE JARGON
In cystic fibrosis the transregulator protein (CFTR) is defective.

THE JARGON
Electrophoresis is a technique used to separate molecules of different electric charge. The speed with which a molecule moves towards an electrode is affected by the amount of the charge and the size of the molecule. Thus, small fragments, with the same charge, move faster than large ones.

GENE THERAPY   ○○○

An example of successful gene therapy involves the treatment of cystic fibrosis.

1	Gene therapy	The CFTR gene codes for a protein which is essential for chloride transport. A defective gene lacks the ability to produce just one particular amino acid.
2	Symptoms	DNA sample collected from blood cells. Copies made using DNA polymerase and run on an electrophoresis gel. The CFTR gene will have a three-base deletion and will move more quickly.
3	Cause	Wrapping the gene in lipid molecules that can pass through the membranes of the lung cells.
4	Diagnostic test	Thick, sticky mucus clogs up the lungs and blocks the pancreatic duct.
5	Treatment	The insertion of a new DNA sequence to counteract a faulty gene.

Describe briefly the purpose of each step in the process.

THE JARGON
The light and dark bands make up the pattern known as the genetic fingerprint.

GENETIC FINGERPRINTING   ○○○

The following are the main stages involved in genetic fingerprinting.

restriction enzymes	
electrophoresis	
radioactive probes	
X-ray film	

Genetic fingerprinting is used in two main areas:

Give two uses of genetic fingerprinting.

IF YOU HAVE TIME
Gather information from a variety of sources and read generally around the subject so that you obtain a balanced viewpoint of this important issue.

The advantages and disadvantages of DNA technology, together with the ethical issues raised will be considered in the exam question section overleaf.

DNA TECHNOLOGY RAISES IMPORTANT SAFETY, MORAL AND ○○○ ETHICAL ISSUES

DNA technology is:

- reshaping medicine and the pharmaceutical industry

- providing forensic, environmental and agricultural applications

- raising important safety and ethical questions.

Turn the page for some exam questions on this topic ➤

EXAM QUESTION 1 ● ● ●

In an investigation involving genetic fingerprinting, DNA was extracted from a blood sample and broken into fragments using a restriction enzyme. The diagram shows the resulting separation of these fragments by electrophoresis.

Interpret this electrophoresis pattern.

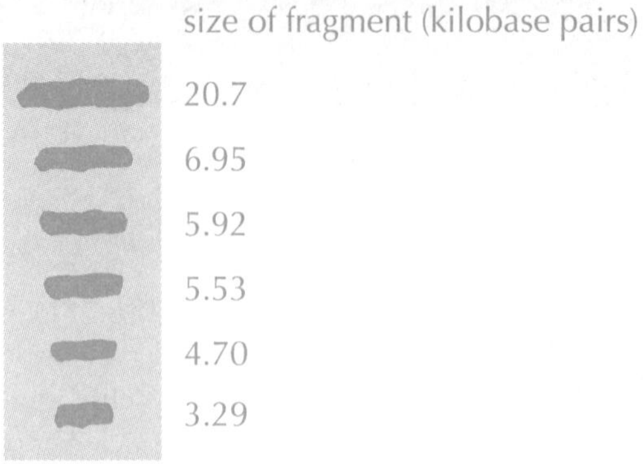

size of fragment (kilobase pairs)

20.7

6.95

5.92

5.53

4.70

3.29

Add an arrow to the diagram to show the direction in which the fragments moved during electrophoresis, giving a reason for your answer.

EXAM QUESTION 2 ● ● ●

There are advantages and disadvantages in DNA technology. Discuss this statement by referring to specific examples wherever possible. These factors might be mentioned in an ideal answer:

Tick the boxes to show which statement is an advantage and which is a disadvantage of DNA technology.

WATCH OUT
Don't confuse the different aspects of DNA technology.

EXAMINER'S SECRETS
These are not all the possible answers. You might think of different ones. There are several ethical issues which have not been mentioned. What is important is that you give biological answers and not philosophical ones.

CHECK THE NET
You'll find information on the Human Genome Program at: www.ornl.gov.TechResources/Human_Genome/home.html

THE JARGON
A pathogen is a disease-causing organism.

IF YOU HAVE TIME
Using the issues raised write an essay to answer question 2.

Factor	Advantantages	Disadvantages
Production of large quantities of complex proteins or peptides, e.g. single cell protein (SCP), insulin.		
Mammalian organs not used in obtaining chemicals, e.g. insulin from pancreas of a cow.		
Expensive to set up on an industrial scale.		
Alleviate symptoms of genetic disease, e.g. cystic fibrosis.		
Genetic analysis may be over emphasized as a predictor of health and false hopes are raised.		
Not all eukaryote genes will express themselves in prokaryote cells.		
Possibility of transfer of DNA with linked pathogenic genes, e.g. oncogenes increasing cancer risks.		
Bacteria readily exchange genetic material, e.g. the deliberate use of antibiotic resistant genes in bacteria could be transferred to pathogens.		
Dispersal and possible cross-fertilization of pollen containing modified gene.		
Unknown effects of eating new protein produced in a crop.		
Producing higher yielding crops with superior keeping qualities and disease resistance.		

Passive transport of molecules

A steady traffic of small molecules moves across the plasma membrane in both directions. Molecules have kinetic energy within them called thermal motion. One result of this thermal motion is diffusion.

THE JARGON
Passive transport does not involve the use of energy.

TRANSPORT PROCESSES ○○○

The processes of passive transport of molecules across a biological membrane include diffusion, osmosis and facilitated diffusion.
Here are definitions of these processes.

Use the correct term for each of the definitions.

EXAMINER'S SECRETS
A useful term is 'concentration gradient' whereby molecules move down a concentration gradient from high to low.

THE JARGON
Water potential (WP) is the capacity of water to leave a system. Pure water has a WP of zero. All solutions have a negative WP.

The process by which a substance moves from where it is more concentrated to where it is less concentrated.	
Diffusion with the help of carrier and channel proteins.	
The movement of water from a solution of less negative water potential to a solution of more negative water potential through a partially permeable membrane.	

DIFFUSION ○○○

The rate of diffusion depends on several factors:

Place a tick alongside one of each pair of factors which will *increase* the rate of diffusion.

DON'T FORGET
Make sure you are familiar with Fick's law.

DON'T FORGET
Polar molecules and ions are impeded by the lipid bilayer of the membrane.

SPEED LEARNING
Think of the o in hypo as being *low* in concentration.

temperature	high		low	
concentration gradient	small		large	
surface area	large		small	
membrane	thin		thick	
pores in membrane	many		few	
solubility in water or lipid	water		lipid	
size of molecules	large		small	

OSMOSIS ○○○

Osmosis in biological systems usually occurs when a membrane separates two solutions of different concentrations. Some terms used are hypertonic, hypotonic and isotonic.

Fill in the blanks A, B and C with the appropriate word.

THE JARGON
Turgid – the vacuole is full of water and the cytoplasm (protoplast) is pushed against the cell wall.

Water moves from a more dilute or . . .A. . . solution to a more concentrated or . . .B. . . solution. When both solutions are of equal concentrations they are said to be . . .C. . . .

A		B		C	

There are differences between plants and animal cells when placed in solutions.

Complete the table and in the space beneath explain the difference in terms of cell structure.

SYLLABUS CHECK
Only the WJEC syllabus requires the use of a *given* equation to determine water potential.

Concentration of solution	Effect on animal cell	Effect on plant cell
hypotonic		
hypertonic		

Turn the page for some exam questions on this topic ➤

EXAM QUESTION 1 ● ● ●

A respiring cell gains oxygen by the process of simple diffusion; it gains most of its glucose by facilitated diffusion.

Try this question which is about diffusion.

IF YOU HAVE TIME
There are a lot of terms and definitions to learn. Make a list of them all on cards or on a chart.

DON'T FORGET
This is Fick's law.

CHECK THE NET
You'll find information on 'the cellular movement of water' at:
carroll1.cc.edu/~jclausz/botany/Water Movement.html

(a) Give one similarity and one difference between the two processes.

Similarity	Difference

(b) The rate of diffusion through a membrane is proportional to:

$$\frac{\text{surface area} \times \text{difference in concentration}}{\text{thickness of membrane}}$$

Suggest whether the values of each of the three variables will be high or low when the rate of diffusion through the membrane is at a minimum.

surface area

difference in concentration

thickness of membrane

EXAM QUESTION 2 ● ● ●

An artificial cell consisting of an aqueous solution enclosed in a selectively permeable membrane has just been immersed in a beaker containing a different solution. The membrane is permeable to water and to the simple sugars glucose and fructose, but completely impermeable to the disaccharide sucrose.

This question tests your understanding of osmosis and diffusion.

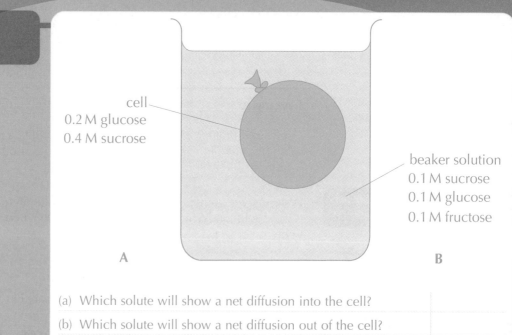

cell
0.2 M glucose
0.4 M sucrose

beaker solution
0.1 M sucrose
0.1 M glucose
0.1 M fructose

A   B

(a) Which solute will show a net diffusion into the cell?

(b) Which solute will show a net diffusion out of the cell?

(c) Which solution, A or B, is hypertonic?

(d) In which direction will there be a net osmotic movement of water?

(e) After the cell is placed in the beaker, will it become flaccid or turgid?

Other methods of molecular transport

There are occasions when molecules need to be transported across the membrane against a concentration gradient, e.g. mineral ion transport. In addition, large molecules such as proteins and polysaccharides generally cross the membrane by entirely different mechanisms involving vesicles.

ACTIVE TRANSPORT ○○○

Active transport takes place via the carrier proteins that span the membrane.

Put the points explaining how a carrier protein operates in active transport in the correct order.

THE JARGON
ATP is often described as the energy currency of the cell. When molecules of ATP are hydrolysed, energy is released for reactions where it is needed in cells.

LINK
For more information on the structure of membranes, see page 23.

1. There is a low concentration of glucose molecules outside the cell.
2. ATP attaches to the membrane protein on the inside of the cell.
3. The protein changes shape (active configuration) and glucose molecules are open to the inside of the membrane and closed to the outside.
4. Glucose molecules are taken up from outside the membrane by being bound to a carrier protein.
5. The carrier protein reverts to its binding configuration.
6. Glucose molecules are released with the aid of energy from ATP.

Any factor which affects the rate of respiration affects the rate of active transport.

Tick the boxes to show whether the rate of active uptake is affected by the factors.

EXAMINER'S SECRETS
You could be asked to explain some or all of these responses in an exam question.
Hints: temperature affects enzymes; cyanide is a respiratory poison.

Factor	Increase rate	Decrease rate
large number of mitochondria		
high concentration of ATP		
low temperature		
high oxygen level		
low concentration of cyanide		

TRANSPORT OF LARGE MOLECULES ○○○

Here are some sentences describing how large molecules enter and leave a cell.

Give the term that describes each process.

SPEED LEARNING
Exo–exit–out.

LINK
For more information on cell organelles, see page 25.

A transport vesicle budded from the Golgi apparatus is moved to the plasma membrane. When they come in contact the two membranes fuse and the contents of the vesicle spills to the outside of the cell.

A small area of the plasma membrane sinks inwards to form a pocket. As the pocket develops, it pinches in, forming a vesicle containing material that had been outside the cell.

A cell engulfs a particle and packages it within a membrane-enclosed sac or vacuole.

A cell engulfs droplets of extracellular fluid in tiny vesicles.

Turn the page for some exam questions on this topic ➤

EXAM QUESTION 1

● ● ●

Measurements were made on the rate of uptake of two different substances, A and B, across the plasma membrane of cells. In each experiment, cells were placed in a known concentration of either A or B and the results of all the experiments are plotted in the graph. At the start of each experiment the internal concentration of A and B within the cells was 50 mM l⁻¹ in each case.

This exam question requires you to interpret the graph. It gets harder as it goes along!

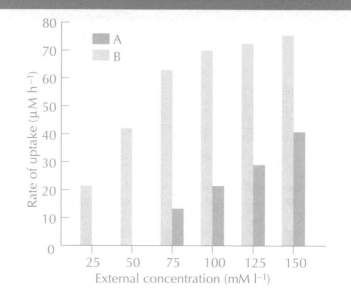

(a) From the graph state the condition that is essential for the transport of A to take place.

(b) What process is responsible for the type of transport shown by A?

(c) (i) What name is given to the type of transport shown by B?

(ii) Give one piece of evidence to support your answer.

IF YOU HAVE TIME
Try this essay question.
'Describe the various ways in which *materials in solution* can cross the membrane boundary of a cell. In *each* case discuss the factors which govern transmission.'

(iii) Apart from B, name *two* other molecules associated with the membrane, which are needed for this process to occur.

(d) (i) Compare the rate of uptake of B between 25 and 50 mM l⁻¹ (external concentration) with the increase between 125 and 150 mM l⁻¹.

WATCH OUT
Be careful to refer to the *rate* of uptake and not just uptake.

(ii) Explain the reason for this difference.

Human digestion

Digestion is the process of breaking down food into molecules small enough for the body to absorb across the intestinal lining into the blood. Some nutrients are transported across the lining by passive means while the absorption of other nutrients is by active transport.

SYLLABUS CHECK
The Edexcel syllabus requires you to study carbohydrate digestion only.

THE HUMAN DIGESTIVE SYSTEM ○○○

This is a simplified diagram of the human gut:

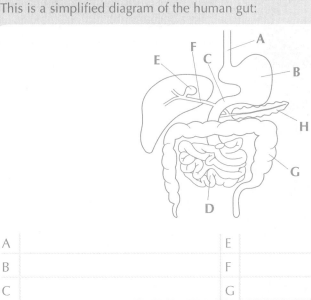

Name the parts labelled A to H.

A		E	
B		F	
C		G	
D		H	

The three main food types are broken down to their basic components by specific enzymes.

Complete the table by giving the names of the enzymes.

Food type	Enzymes	Action of enzyme
carbohydrate		starch to maltose maltose to glucose
protein	peptidase:	hydrolyse peptide bonds *between* amino acids in the central region of proteins
		hydrolyse peptide bonds on the terminal amino acids of the portions, progressively reducing them to individual amino acids
fat		lipids to fatty acids and glycerol

LINK
For more information on enzymes see page 15.

SYLLABUS CHECK
The Edexcel syllabus requires you to study the histology of the ileum wall. The AQA(B) syllabus requires you to know about the generalized structure of the human gut wall as well as features of the different regions.

ABSORPTION ○○○

Efficient absorption is dependent in part on a large surface area being available.

List four adaptations of the wall of the ileum for efficient absorption.

LINK
For more information on molecular transport mechanisms see pages 35 and 37.

Turn the page for some exam questions on this topic ➤

EXAM QUESTION 1 ● ● ●

Try this recall question. Complete the table, which summarizes the digestion of selected substrates.

Enzyme	Site of secretion	Substrate	Products
	stomach	protein	polypeptides/peptides
exopeptidase	pancreas	peptides	
amylase	intestinal gland		maltose

EXAM QUESTION 2 ● ● ●

This question concentrates on fat digestion and absorption.

(a) Name the region of the digestive system where most fat digestion occurs.

(b) Name the enzyme which is responsible for the digestion of fat.

(c) Name the site of secretion of this enzyme.

(d) Describe fully the part played by liver in the digestion of fat.

(e) Describe how digested lipids may be absorbed from the gut.

EXAM QUESTION 3 ● ● ●

The electron micrograph diagram shows some of the cells forming part of the epithelial lining of the human small intestine.

Study the diagram carefully before answering the question.

SYLLABUS CHECK
Check that your syllabus requires you to be able to interpret electron micrograph diagrams *in this topic.*

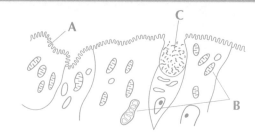

(a) Name the features labelled A and B and explain how they function in this tissue.

A

B

(b) Name the secretion labelled C.

Transport and exchange mechanisms

Living things need to obtain materials such as carbon dioxide and oxygen from the environment and remove waste from their cells to the environment. Efficient exchange mechanisms require the surface area over which transfer is to occur to be large compared with the volume of the organism.

SPEED LEARNING

If you find the concept of surface area to volume ratio difficult, consider it this way. *If the overall shape is kept the same, an increase in size means an increased distance from the surface to the centre of the organism.*

SIZE AND SURFACE AREA ○○○

With increase in size the surface area to volume ratio is decreased and exchange demand by simple diffusion is inadequate. An increase in metabolic rate also makes diffusion insufficient to supply demand. The table shows various dimensions of animal tissue.

> Using the information in the table, state in words, the *quantitative* relationship between length and surface area:volume ratio.

Length of side (cm)	Volume (cm³)	Ratio of surface area:volume
1	1	6:1
2	8	3:1
3	27	2:1

> Complete the table that summarizes how different animals have overcome the problem of obtaining materials from the environment.

Organism	Surface area: volume ratio	Modification	Exchange surface
unicellular protozoan		small	
flatworm	large		surface
earthworm	small		moist skin
fish	small	specialized exchange surface	
mammal	small	specialized exchange surface	

LINK

For more information on diffusion, see page 35.

THE EXCHANGE SURFACE ○○○

The requirements of an efficient exchange surface:

> List the requirements of an efficient respiratory exchange surface.

LINK

Specialized exchange surfaces are dealt with in more detail on page 43.

In addition animals which have evolved specialized exchange surfaces need:

> List the additional requirements of fish and mammals.

Turn the page for some exam questions on this topic ➤

EXAM QUESTION 1 ●●●

Diagram A illustrates the size and shape of *Amoeba* (a single celled organism) and diagram B illustrates *Planaria* (a flatworm).

Have a go at answering a question about diffusion in small organisms.

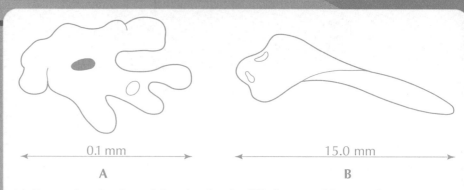

|←——— 0.1 mm ———→| |←——— 15.0 mm ———→|

A   B

(a) For each animal, explain why simple diffusion provides an adequate gaseous exchange between the organism and its environment.

Amoeba

Planaria

(b) Explain why both animals can only exist in water.

EXAM QUESTION 2 ●●●

This question requires you to consider adaptations needed to overcome an increase in size.

(a) Explain why an increase in size in animals makes respiratory exchange more difficult.

(b) Suggest three different ways in which animals overcome this problem.

Gas exchange in bony fish

Fish obtain oxygen from water by means of gills.

GILL STRUCTURE ○○○

The diagram shows the operculum (gill cover) removed to show the gills.

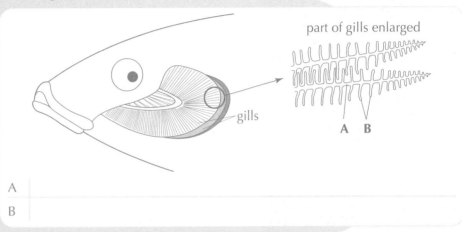

part of gills enlarged

gills

A B

Label parts A and B.

A

B

The gills also have an extensive network of blood capillaries to allow efficient diffusion, and haemoglobin for the carriage of oxygen.

VENTILATION MECHANISM ○○○

Water is a dense medium with a low oxygen content, so it needs to be forced over the gill filaments by pressure differences. This maintains a continuous, unidirectional flow of water.

Complete the table by inserting the appropriate word.

DON'T FORGET
A lower pressure is maintained in the opercular cavity than in the bucco-pharynx.
The operculum acts as both a valve permitting water out and as a pump drawing water past the gill filaments. The mouth also acts as a pump and together with the actions of the operculum, delivers an almost continuous flow of water over the gills.

	Water intake	Water expulsion
mouth	opens	
operculum		
floor of buccal cavity		
volume	increases	decreases
pressure		

COUNTER CURRENT FLOW ○○○

Efficient gaseous exchange is achieved by the stream of water flowing over the gills and the blood flow through the gills being in opposite directions:

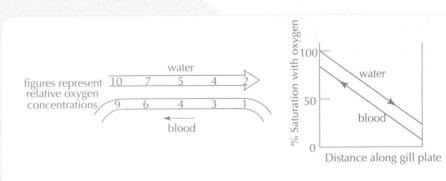

figures represent relative oxygen concentrations

water
10   7   5   4   2

9   6   4   3   1
blood

% Saturation with oxygen

100

water

50

blood

0

Distance along gill plate

Explain how the counter current flow increases the efficiency of gaseous exchange.

Turn the page for some exam questions on this topic ➤

The diagram shows a structure adapted for gaseous exchange.

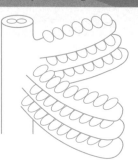

You should find this first question quite easy.

(a) Name the group of animals in which the structure is found.

(b) State two features of the structure which aid efficient gaseous exchange.

EXAMINER'S SECRETS
Since the question asks you to *state* rather than *explain* there is no need to go into the details of the ventilation mechanism here.

(c) State how a continuous supply of oxygen reaches the surface of the structure.

(d) Explain why the structure could not function in a land animal.

The diagram shows a gill plate of a bony fish.

This question covers the same topic but goes into more detail.

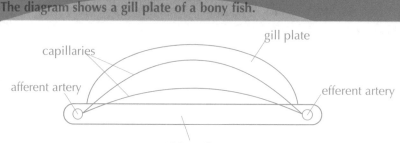

capillaries

gill plate

afferent artery

efferent artery

gill lamella (TS)

(a) (i) Draw arrows on the capillaries to indicate the direction of the blood flow.

(ii) Draw and label an arrow to indicate the flow of water over the gill plate.

(b) Describe three ways, other than the flow arrangement, in which the gill filament is adapted as a respiratory surface.

Gas exchange in plants

To make food a plant must provide a large surface area, the leaves, to the sun and obtain carbon dioxide from the air. CO_2 diffuses into the leaf, and O_2, produced as a by-product of photosynthesis, diffuses out of the leaf through the stomata.

LEAF STRUCTURE   ○○○

The diagram is a transverse section of a leaf.

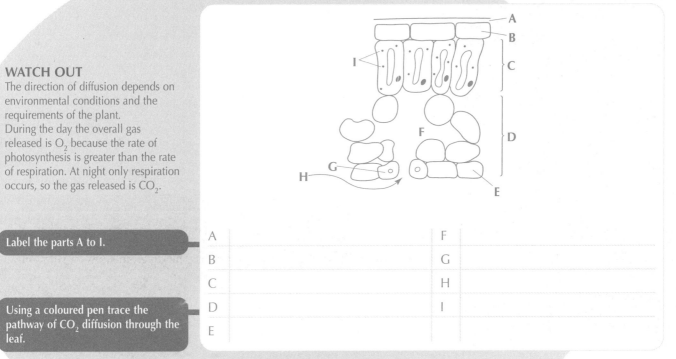

WATCH OUT
The direction of diffusion depends on environmental conditions and the requirements of the plant.
During the day the overall gas released is O_2 because the rate of photosynthesis is greater than the rate of respiration. At night only respiration occurs, so the gas released is CO_2.

> Label the parts A to I.

A		F	
B		G	
C		H	
D		I	
E			

> Using a coloured pen trace the pathway of CO_2 diffusion through the leaf.

The leaf is well adapted for gaseous exchange.

> List three ways in which the leaf is adapted for efficient gas exchange.

MECHANISM OF OPENING AND CLOSING OF STOMATA   ○○○

Guard cells, by controlling the opening and closing of stomata, help balance the plant's need to conserve water with its requirement for photosynthesis.

> Starting with statement 1 place the stages of the *opening* mechanism of stomata in the correct order.

1. In the light, guard cells increase their turgor by actively transporting potassium ions (K^+) from adjacent cells to the guard cells.

2. K^+ ions lower the water potential and cause water to move in by osmosis.

3. The pairs of cells curve away from each other and the pore opens.

4. The pumping of K^+ ions requires energy.

5. Guard cells become turgid and swell.

6. Guard cells do not expand uniformly as the inner wall is thicker and less elastic than the outer wall.

7. Energy is provided from photosynthesis and this is why guard cells contain chloroplasts.

DON'T FORGET
Guard cells control the diameter of the stoma by changing shape, thereby narrowing or widening the gap between the two cells. They are the only cells in the epidermal layer to contain chloroplasts.

SYLLABUS CHECK
Skip the mechanism if you're studying the AQA(B) syllabus.

Turn the page for some exam questions on this topic ➤

EXAMINER'S SECRETS
You will lose marks if you do not provide a diagram (and of good quality).

EXAM QUESTION 1

● ● ●

Give an illustrated account of the structure of the leaf (excluding vascular tissue) as seen in a high power section. Describe how the structure of the leaf is related to its function.

These factors might be mentioned in an ideal answer.

Fill in the boxes with the appropriate leaf structure

waterproofing layer	
layer of protection	
site of photosynthesis	
site of gaseous diffusion	
allow passage of gases between cells and outside via stomata	
diffusion of O_2, CO_2 and water vapour in and out of leaf	
aid in opening and closing mechanism	
large surface area, thin for gas exchange and trapping of light	
contain pigments to trap light	

IF YOU HAVE TIME
Use the table to write out a *full* answer to the question. Include a diagram similar to that on the previous page.

EXAM QUESTION 2

● ● ●

Stomata are found on the underside of leaves. The diagram shows a stoma in surface view.

This question concentrates on the stomata.

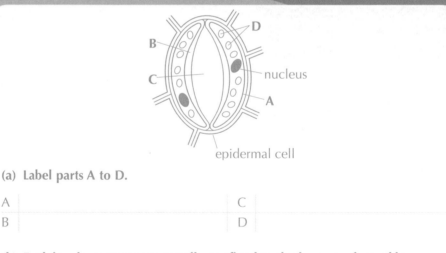

(a) Label parts A to D.

A		C	
B		D	

(b) Explain why stomata are usually confined to the lower surface of leaves.

(c) Explain how the opening and closing mechanism of stomata is related to the *structure* of the guard cells.

Gas exchange in mammals

Mammals are active and have evolved internal lungs which are adapted for exchange with air, a less dense medium than water.

STRUCTURE OF RESPIRATORY SYSTEM   ○○○

The diagram shows the human respiratory system.

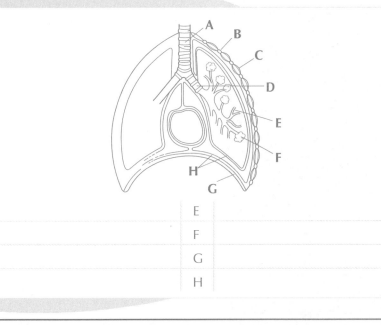

Label the parts A to H.

DON'T FORGET
Lungs supply a large surface area, increased by alveoli, lined with moisture for the dissolving of gases, thin walls to shorten diffusion path and an extensive capillary network for rapid diffusion and transport, to maintain diffusion gradients.

A		E	
B		F	
C		G	
D		H	

VENTILATION OF THE LUNGS   ○○○

Mammals ventilate their lungs by negative pressure breathing, forcing air down into the lungs.

Complete the table to show how pressure changes are achieved in the thorax.

SYLLABUS CHECK
Control of breathing is required by the AQA(A), AQA(B) and Edexcel syllabuses.

	Inspiration	Expiration
external intercostal muscle		
ribs		
diaphragm		
volume of thorax		
pressure in thorax		
outside air (atmospheric) pressure	Greater, therefore air moves in	Less, therefore air moves out

LUNG CAPACITY   ○○○

Terms are used to describe the different volumes of air held in the lungs.

Complete the table, giving the appropriate term used to describe the volume of air exchanged.

DON'T FORGET
The pattern of change in lung volume during human breathing can be analysed using an instrument called a spirometer.

Term	Volume (dm³)	
		normal breathing
inspiratory reserve volume	2.0	deepest breath in (A)
expiratory reserve volume	1.5	deepest breath out (B)
	3.5	volume between A and B
	1.5	lungs are never empty

Turn the page for some exam questions on this topic ➤

47

BIOLOGY

EXAM QUESTION 1 ●●●

The diagram shows part of the wall of an alveolus and a section across a blood capillary.

> This question is about gas exchange in the lungs.

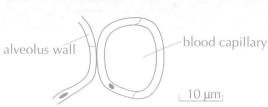

alveolus wall

blood capillary

10 µm

(a) Name the process by which oxygen passes from the alveolus to the capillary.

(b) The width of the wall of the alveolus and the flow of blood in the capillary both affect the efficiency of the process.
Explain how each affects the process.

width of the wall

flow of blood

(c) As the carbon dioxide concentration in the alveoli increases, the amount of air taken in by respiratory movements also increases. State two ways in which the respiratory movements change to achieve this effect.

EXAM QUESTION 2 ●●●

Each of the graphs shows a trace obtained on a spirometer's recording apparatus. Each peak shows the volume of air breathed in and each trough shows the volume breathed out. The small fluctuations show breathing in a resting person, the large fluctuations show the maximum inhalation and expiration the person could achieve. Trace A was obtained from a healthy person and trace B from a typical asthma sufferer.

> Look back at the definitions on the previous page before attempting this question.

A

Volume (dm³)
7
6
5
4
3
2
1
0
0 2 4 6 8 10 12 14 16 18 20
Time (seconds)

B

Volume (dm³)
7
6
5
4
3
2
1
0
0 2 4 6 8 10 12 14 16 18 20
Time (seconds)

(a) For the healthy subject give:

the tidal volume

the vital capacity

(b) Compare the normal trace and the trace for the asthma sufferer.
Give two ways in which the traces differ and one way in which they are the same.

Differences

Similarity

Blood

Blood is a type of connective tissue consisting of several types of cells suspended in a liquid matrix called plasma.

FUNCTIONS OF BLOOD ○○○

Blood carries out a number of functions.

Complete the table, listing the appropriate blood component.

SYLLABUS CHECK
Skip the transport of respiratory gases if you're studying the AQA(A) syllabus.

DON'T FORGET
Granulocytes and lymphocytes are different types of leucocytes.

THE JARGON
Buffering prevents harmful changes in pH.

Blood component	Function
	transport of materials e.g. digested food, urea, CO_2 etc.
erythrocytes	
	phagocytosis
lymphocytes	

TRANSPORT OF CO_2 – THE CHLORIDE SHIFT ○○○

In addition to its role in O_2 transport, haemoglobin also helps the blood transport CO_2 and assists in buffering the blood.

The reaction steps in the table take place in either the red blood cells or the plasma. State the appropriate site in the boxes.

THE JARGON
RBC is an abbreviation for red blood cell.

DON'T FORGET
The majority of the carbon dioxide produced by the tissues combines with water to form carbonic acid. This reaction is catalysed by the enzyme carbonic anhydrase.

DON'T FORGET
The pH decreases (becomes more acidic) in very active tissues because the CO_2 produced by respiration reacts with water to form carbonic acid, which dissociates to give H^+ and HCO_3^-.

Reaction site	Reaction
RBC	CO_2 + water = carbonic acid
	carbonic acid dissociates into H^+ and HCO_3^-
RBC/plasma	HCO_3^- diffuses out of RBC
	NaCl dissociates into Na^+ and Cl^-
	HCO_3^- + Na^+ = sodium hydrogen carbonate
	H^+ encourages HbO_2 to dissociate to Hb + O_2
	H^+ + Hb = HHb O_2 diffuses out of RBC into tissues
	To balance outward movement of negative ions, chloride ions diffuse in.

OXYGEN TRANSPORT – THE BOHR EFFECT ○○○

The release of oxygen from haemoglobin is aided by the presence of carbon dioxide. The graph shows the oxygen dissociation curve for haemoglobin.

Interpret the graph, then complete the table. Notice how more oxygen is released when the curve shifts to the right.

EXAMINER'S SECRETS
At pH 7.4 and at a pO_2 of 40 mm Hg, haemoglobin is only 75% saturated, i.e. it gives up 24% of its O_2 to the tissues (99 − 75 = 24)

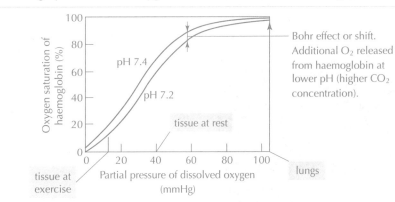

Bohr effect or shift. Additional O_2 released from haemoglobin at lower pH (higher CO_2 concentration).

pO_2 (mmHg)	% Saturation		% O_2 released	
	at pH 7.4	at pH 7.2	at pH 7.4	at pH 7.2
104 (in lungs)	98	− − −	− − −	− − −
40 (in tissues)	75	65	24	
10 (muscle tissue)				

Turn the page for some exam questions on this topic ➤

EXAM QUESTION 1

The oxygen dissociation curve of human haemoglobin for a normal person at rest at 37°C and for a human fetus are shown in the graph.

If you are sure you understand the oxygen dissociation curve, have a go at this question.

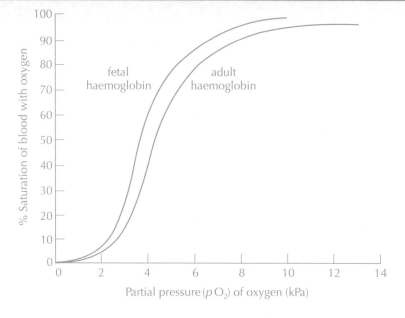

THE JARGON
Oxygen concentration is measured by partial pressure, otherwise called the oxygen tension.
The units are kiloPascals or kPa.

(a) State the % saturation of adult blood with oxygen when pO_2 is:

4 kPa   6 kPa

(b) How would the dissociation curve differ if the blood had a high concentration of carbon dioxide?

(c) What is the significance of this difference?

(d) What is the importance of the fetus having a haemoglobin that differs from that of the adult?

(e) Where would the dissociation curve for myoglobin be in relation to that for adult Hb? Give an explanation for your answer.

(f) Where would the dissociation curve for a llama be in relation to that of the adult human? Explain your answer.

Blood vessels

There are three types of blood vessel. Arteries carry blood away from the heart, veins carry blood to the heart and the much smaller capillaries link arteries to veins.

> Complete the table by using the information provided in the text.

> Draw arrows on the diagram to show:
> • the direction of blood flow
> • the direction and destination of tissue fluid.

> Explain the forces involved in pressure filtration

STRUCTURE AND FUNCTION OF BLOOD VESSELS   ○○○

Structural differences in the walls of the different blood vessels correlate with their different functions.

Arteries have thick muscular, elastic walls. They need strength and elasticity to accommodate changes in blood flow and pressure.

Veins have fewer elastic and muscular fibres in their walls. Blood flows in them back to the heart at low velocity and pressure. Skeletal muscles squeeze the veins and valves prevent backflow.

Capillaries possess a wall which is only one cell thick, allowing rapid exchange of materials by diffusion. Blood flow is slowed in them because their total cross-sectional area is much greater than in arteries.

Feature	Artery	Vein	Capillary
muscle layer			none
elastic layer			
lumen (relative to diameter)			
valves	no	yes	
permeability	no		yes
blood pressure			reducing
blood flow			slowing

EXCHANGE OF MATERIALS BETWEEN CAPILLARIES AND TISSUE FLUID   ○○○

The diagram shows the formation and destination of tissue fluid:

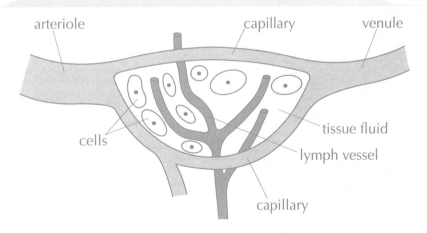

arteriole   capillary   venule
cells   tissue fluid   lymph vessel   capillary

Exchange takes place in the capillary beds by pressure filtration:

Turn the page for some exam questions on this topic ➤

EXAM QUESTION 1   ●●●

Diagrams A, B and C show cross sections of three different types of blood vessels. They are not drawn to the same scale.

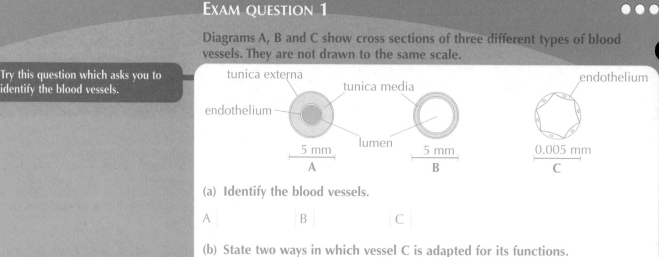

(a) Identify the blood vessels.

A | B | C |

(b) State two ways in which vessel C is adapted for its functions.

EXAM QUESTION 2   ●●●

The table shows the maximum and minimum blood pressures (in kPa) at various points in selected arteries and capillaries.

DON'T FORGET
The pulmonary artery carries blood from the lungs back to the heart.

Site	Blood pressure (kPa)	
	Maximum	Minimum
pulmonary artery	3.33	1.07
muscle capillary	2.00	2.00
lung capillary	1.07	0.67

(a) There is a difference between arterial pressures and the capillary pressures. Explain, in relation to the *functions* of these vessels, why this is more efficient.

(b) (i) Compare the values for capillaries in the muscle with capillaries in the lung.

(ii) Suggest why these differences occur.

DON'T FORGET
The muscular wall of the left ventricle of the heart is about three times as thick as that of the right ventricle. This difference is related to the greater distance that blood is pumped by the left ventricle, and the resistance that it has to overcome in serving the whole body.

(c) Give one reason to explain how a return flow to the heart is possible when the vein pressures are so low.

The heart

Each day the heart beats up to 100 000 times and pumps out 13 000 dm³ of blood.

THE CARDIAC CYCLE   ○○○

The cardiac muscles of the heart contract and relax in a rhythmic cycle.

Fill in the missing words.

When the heart ...A... it pumps blood and when it ...B... its chambers fill with blood. One complete sequence of pumping and filling is called the ...C... cycle. A contraction phase of the cycle is called ...D..., and a relaxation phase is called ...E....

A		B		C	
D		E			

IF YOU HAVE TIME
Draw a section through the heart and from memory label the chambers, valves and associated blood vessels. Use a coloured pen to show the circulation of blood through the heart.

The myogenic stimulation of the heart is maintained by the transmission of a wave of electrical activity. Three groups of tissues are involved.

THE JARGON
The heart muscle is *myogenic,* that is, the heart beat is initiated from within the muscle itself and is not due to nervous stimulation.

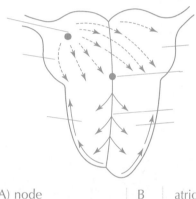

Label A to G on the diagram. Labels D to G are the chambers of the heart.

A	sinoatrial (SA) node	B	atrioventricular node
C	bundle of His	D	left atrium
E	left ventricle	F	right ventricle
G	right atrium		

THE JARGON
Another term for atrium is auricle.

Place steps 1 to 6 of the control of heartbeat (cardiac cycle) in the correct order.

1. The impulses are delayed at the AV node for about 0.1 seconds, during which blood in the atria empties into the ventricles.
2. The ventricles contract simultaneously from the apex upwards.
3. Blood is driven into the large arteries.
4. The new wave of excitation from the AV node is conducted along Purkyne fibres which collectively make up the bundle of His.
5. The fibres conduct impulses to the apex of the heart and throughout the ventricular walls.
6. The SA node generates electrical impulses that spread through both atria, making them contract simultaneously.

THE JARGON
'Purkyne' is spelt 'Purkinje' in some textbooks.

THE JARGON
Stroke volume is the amount of blood pumped by the left ventricle each time it contracts.

FACTORS MODIFYING HEART RATE   ○○○

If the stroke volume is 75 millilitres and the heart rate is 70 beats per minute, use the equation to calculate the cardiac output per minute.

The cardiac output can be calculated using an equation:

Cardiac output = heart rate (pulse) × stroke volume =

List two different body systems that can modify heart rate.

Turn the page for some exam questions on this topic ➤

EXAM QUESTION 1 ●●●

This question asks about some general features of heart structure and function.

(a) State three essential features of a circulating mass flow system.

(b) State an advantage of

    (i) a double circulation system

    (ii) a four-chambered heart.

(c) Describe and explain

    (i) the difference between the pressure of the blood leaving the left ventricle (LV) and the pressure of the blood leaving the right ventricle (RV).

    (ii) the relationship between the cardiac output of the left side of the heart and the cardiac output of the right side of the heart.

EXAM QUESTION 2 ●●●

The diagram shows a normal electrocardiogram (ECG) for one heartbeat.

This question requires you to have a good understanding of the control of the cardiac cycle.

THE JARGON
An electrocardiogram shows the pattern of electrical activity associated with a heart.

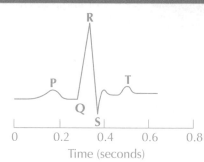

P represents the electrical activity as it passes over the atria.

Q, R and S represent the spread of electrical activity over the ventricles.
T indicates the electrical recovery of the ventricles.

(a) Give the name of the tissue of the heart represented by the electrical activity at Q R S.

(b) There is a delay of 0.1 seconds between P and Q. Explain what causes this delay and why it is important in the functioning of the heart.

(c) What is happening to the blood in the heart during T?

Transport in plants

In plants the roots, which collect the water, are some distance from the leaves that require it for photosynthesis. A transport system of specialized cells connects the two structures.

STRUCTURE OF THE STEM

○○○

The diagram shows a transverse section (T.S.) through a typical dicotyledonous stem.

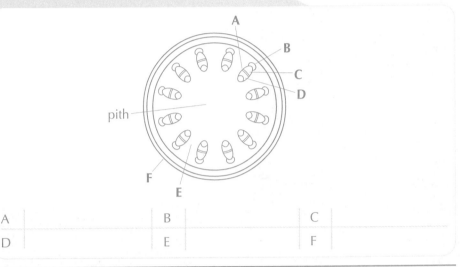

Label parts A to F in the diagram.

A		B		C	
D		E		F	

IF YOU HAVE TIME
Your practical work with the microscope should be studied in conjunction with this section. Draw xylem and phloem in transverse section (T.S.) and longitudinal section (L.S.) and be able to distinguish and identify cells in the two views.

LINKS
For more information on leaf structure, see page 45.

CHECK THE NET
You'll find information and exercises on plant cell types and organs at: wsuonline.weber.edu/course.botany.130/unit1_la.htm

STRUCTURE OF THE ROOT

○○○

The diagram shows a T.S. through a root.

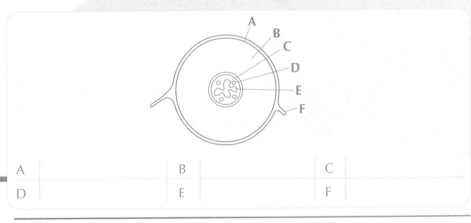

Label parts A to F in the diagram.

A		B		C	
D		E		F	

STRUCTURE OF VASCULAR TISSUES

○○○

Xylem tissue consists of four different types of cells.

List the cells which make up xylem and phloem and give the functions of the *two* main cells in each tissue.

1.
2.
3.
4.

Phloem tissue also consists of four different types of cells.

EXAMINER'S SECRETS
A thorough understanding of xylem and phloem cell structure is essential to enable you to answer questions on the mechanisms of transport in plants.

1.
2.
3.
4.

Turn the page for some exam questions on this topic ➤

For more on this topic, see page 42 of the *Revision Express A-level Study Guide*

EXAM QUESTION 1

Diagrams A and B represent T.S. stem and T.S. root, showing the distribution of the main tissue types.

Try this question which asks you to distinguish between the root and stem.

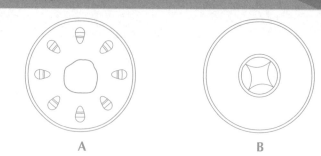

A   B

(a) Which diagram A, or B, is the T.S. stem? Give a reason for your answer.

(B) Write the name of the different tissues which carry out the functions below.

transport of sugars	
transport of water	
cell division	

EXAM QUESTION 2

The statements refer to specific cells found in xylem and phloem.

If the statement is correct place a tick in the appropriate box.

Statement	Xylem vessels	Sieve tubes
provide support		
walls contain lignin		
transport in one direction		
made up of cells joined end to end		
possess living contents		

EXAM QUESTION 3

The diagrams show sections through the same tissue in a dicotyledonous stem.

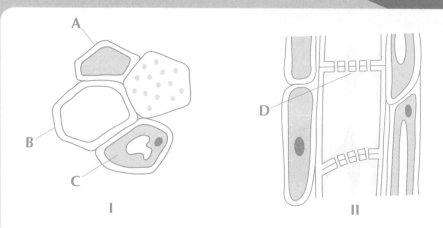

I   II

(a) Name the cell types labelled A to C on diagram I.

A   B   C

(b) Label equivalent cells A and B on diagram II.

(c) What is structure D?

Transport of water through the plant

Water from the soil enters the plant through the epidermis of the root, crosses the root cortex, passes into the xylem of the vascular bundle and then flows up the xylem vessels to the shoot system and to the leaves.

WATER TRANSPORT ACROSS THE ROOT CORTEX ○○○

Once water enters the root, by a combination of soaking into the epidermal cells and osmosis, it travels across the cortex. The diagram shows the three routes for water transport across cells.

vacuole cytoplasm cell wall

Complete the table to identify the three pathways of water transport through cells.

	Pathway	Cell structure
A		
B		
C		

DON'T FORGET
A water potential gradient exists across the cortex. The WP is high in the root hair cells and lower in the adjacent cells.

THE JARGON
The Casparian strip is made of suberin which is a waxy material that is impervious to water and dissolved minerals.

IF YOU HAVE TIME
Make notes on the active uptake of mineral ions and their movement in the transpiration stream.

Explain the role of the endodermis as a selective sentry between the root cortex and the vascular tissue by filling in the blanks in the description.

THE ROLE OF THE ENDODERMIS ○○○

The endodermis blocks the apoplast pathway and regulates the ions which the plant draws into the xylem. The diagram shows two views of endodermal cells.

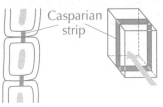

Casparian strip

direction in which water passes through endodermal cell

Water and minerals can only get past the barrier by being diverted into the ...A... pathway. Since the xylem lacks cell contents the entry of water and minerals into the xylem require their return to the ...B... pathway in the cells internal to the endodermis. Diffusion and ...C... are thought to be involved in the transfer of solutes.

A   B   C

THE COHESION–TENSION THEORY ○○○

Evaporation of water from the leaves provides the pull and the cohesion of water transmits the upward pull along the length of the xylem to the roots.

List the forces which contribute to the movement of water up the stem.

water loss from leaf drawing water from the xylem	
hydrogen bonding between water molecules	
forces between the water molecules and the walls of the xylem vessels	

Turn the page for some exam questions on this topic ➤

EXAM QUESTION 1

●●●

This question is quite straightforward. It does not ask for much detail.

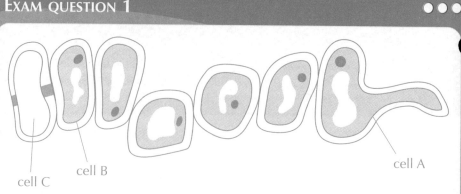

cell C   cell B   cell A

The diagram shows some root cells in a transverse section.

(a) Explain briefly, in terms of water potential, how water moves from the soil into cell A.

IF YOU HAVE TIME
Draw a diagram of a plant showing the roots, stem and leaves. On it show the pathway of water and indicate the active and passive processes which take place at the appropriate points.

(b) Draw a line on the diagram to show the apoplast pathway through these cells.

(c) Cell C is the innermost layer of cells of the cortex.

Give the name of this layer.

EXAM QUESTION 2

●●●

Describe the route taken by water travelling from the soil to the leaf and the forces involved in this movement.

These factors might be mentioned in an ideal answer.

Try planning this essay question. It's quite tricky.

IF YOU HAVE TIME
Use the statements to write out your essay.

DON'T FORGET
Long distance transport of water from roots to leaves occurs by mass flow, the movement of water driven by a pressure difference at opposite ends of a continuous system of channels, formed by the vessels and tracheids.

materials move in solution with a combined push from below and pull from above	force/process involved
active transport establishes an osmotic gradient across apoplast of cortex	root pressure
removal of ions from apoplast of cortex into symplast (causing low concentration)	active transport
water moves through cells via plasmodesmata into stele	a high osmotic gradient is created
leak from stele back into apoplast (causing high concentration)	no force involved
bonding between water molecules	cohesion resulting in 'pull'
bonding between water and hydrophilic walls of vessels	adhesion
very small diameter of vessels and tracheids	capillarity
evaporation of water from leaves	transpiration
replacement of water from below as a mass flow	transpiration pull

Transpiration

About 99% of the water moving through the plant is lost from the leaves as water vapour. This evaporation of water through the stomata of the leaves is known as transpiration.

THE ROLE OF TRANSPIRATION

○○○

Water loss is a consequence of having pores in the leaf to allow the exchange of gases for photosynthesis. However, it also has useful functions in the plant.

> **List three ways in which transpiration contributes to the functioning of the plant**

DON'T FORGET
Some water is also lost through the cuticle.

FACTORS AFFECTING TRANSPIRATION RATE

○○○

Water vapour diffuses from a region of high WP to a region of low WP down a water potential gradient. The diagram shows this situation in a section of a typical leaf.

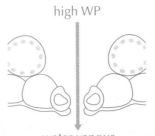

high WP

water vapour
low WP in atmospheric air

Any factor which alters the size of the gradient will influence the rate of transpiration.

> **Tick the boxes to indicate if there is an increase or decrease in transpiration under the conditions shown.**

DON'T FORGET
The water potential of the atmosphere is determined by the interaction of these factors.

Condition	Increase	Decrease
high humidity		
increase in light intensity		
still air		
high temperature		

LINK
For more information on opening and closing of stomata, see page 45. This is the means by which the plant *controls* transpiration.

XEROPHYTES

○○○

Xerophytes have adapted to living under conditions of low water availability and so have modified structures to prevent excessive water loss:

> **Describe the specific effect of the modification (where possible in terms of how it affects the WP gradient).**

SYLLABUS CHECK
Skip xerophytes if you're studying the Edexcel syllabus.
The WJEC syllabus requires you to study a specific example, marram grass.

Feature that minimizes water loss	Effect
thick leaf cuticle	
layer of epidermal hairs	
sunken stomata	
rolled leaf	

Turn the page for some exam questions on this topic ➤

EXAM QUESTION 1 ● ● ●

Graphs A, B and C give the effect of three external conditions on the rate of transpiration in plants.

Have a go at this question concerning factors that affect the rate of transpiration.

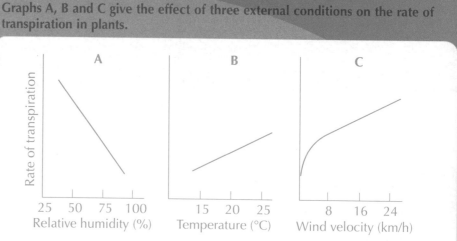

Describe how each factor influences the rate of transpiration.

DON'T FORGET
You should describe the effect in terms of water potential gradient.

Graph A

Graph B

Graph C

EXAM QUESTION 2 ● ● ●

The 'Two-leaf Hakea' is a plant found in south-west Australia, where the spring is relatively cool and wet but the summer is very hot and dry. The plant produces one type of leaf in spring (A) and a different type (B) in the summer. The table shows the average values of a range of measurements taken from the leaves.

This question is about how a xerophyte is adapted to cope with periods of water stress.

Characteristic of leaf	A	B
length (mm)	33	55
maximum width (mm)	10	0.8
surface area (mm²)	292	144
volume (mm³)	64	63
cuticle thickness (μm)	14	24

(a) Calculate the surface area (SA) to volume ratio for leaves A and B.

    A   B

(b) Use the data in the table to list four ways in which leaf type B is adapted to summer conditions in south-west Australia.

(c) Suggest and explain one advantage to the plant of producing leaf type A in the spring.

Translocation

There is considerable controversy regarding the mechanism by which materials are translocated in phloem. However, it is agreed that the observed rate of flow is much too fast for diffusion to be the cause.

MECHANISM OF TRANSLOCATION   ○○○

The diagram shows a model which is used to explain how organic substances move through a plant. A and B represent cells surrounded by membranes permeable only to water.

Complete the diagram by adding arrow heads to the lines in the diagram to show the direction in which fluid will move (at A, B, C and D).

LINK
For more information on the structure of phloem, see page 55.

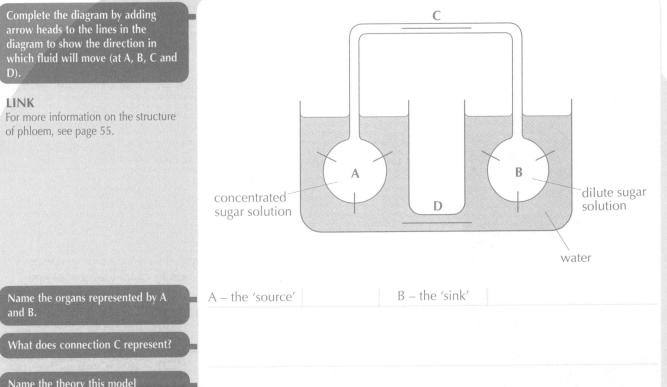

concentrated sugar solution

dilute sugar solution

water

Name the organs represented by A and B.

A – the 'source'	B – the 'sink'

What does connection C represent?

Name the theory this model represents.

Fill in the blanks to help explain the theory.

At the source, phloem companion cells actively take up sucrose and pass it to sieve tubes while the reverse process occurs at the sink. This causes a concentration gradient from source to sink. Phloem loading causes a high solute concentration at the source end of the sieve tube, which ...A... the water potential (WP) and causes water to flow into the tube by the process of ...B.... Hydrostatic pressure develops within the sieve tube and the pressure is greatest at the source end. At the sink end sucrose concentration ...C..., as it is being utilized or converted to ...D... for storage. These cells then have a higher WP and consequently a lower hydrostatic pressure. At the sink end the pressure is relieved by the loss of water. The building of pressure at the source and the reduction of that pressure at the sink causes water to move from ...E... to ...F... carrying the sucrose along.

WATCH OUT
A lowering of WP means that it becomes more negative.

THE JARGON
Hydrostatic pressure can also be referred to as pressure potential.

A	B	C
D	E	F

Turn the page for some exam questions on this topic ➤

EXAM QUESTION 1   ● ● ●

The diagram illustrates the mass flow hypothesis which has been suggested to explain the movement of substances in the phloem.

Have a go at explaining the mass flow hypothesis.

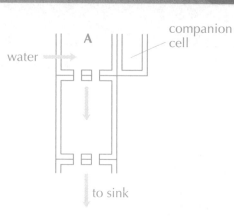

(a) Suggest a plant organ which is a source.

(b) There are companion cells alongside the phloem sieve tube at A. Explain what causes water to move into the phloem at A.

(c) From your knowledge of the mass flow hypothesis how would you expect the movement of carbohydrates in the phloem to change over a 24 hour period?

EXAM QUESTION 2   ● ● ●

Review the evidence for and against the mass flow hypothesis.

These factors might be mentioned in an ideal answer.

Tick the boxes to show which statements support the hypothesis and which contradict it.

	Supports	Contradicts
Sieve plate hinders mass flow.		
ATP is consumed by the companion cells.		
Some researchers have observed mass flow under the microscope in the phloem.		
Viruses or growth chemicals applied to leaves are only translocated downwards during periods of photosynthesis.		
Sucrose and amino acids have been observed to move at different speeds and in different directions in the same vascular bundles.		
Gradients exist in the concentration of sucrose between source and sink.		
The contents of phloem sieve tubes are under pressure and sap exudes when phloem tissue is cut.		

IF YOU HAVE TIME
Use the statements to write out your essay.

SYLLABUS CHECK
Only the WJEC syllabus requires an awareness of other theories proposed.

Ecosystems and energy

Energy enters an ecosystem, flows within it, and eventually exits from it.

THE ECOSYSTEM ○○○

The following are the definitions of some terms used in the study of ecosystems.

Give the correct term for each definition.

A group of individuals of one species occupying a particular area.	
A particular area occupied by a population.	
All the organisms that inhabit a particular area.	
All the organisms living in a community as well as all the abiotic factors with which they interact.	
The feeding level in a food chain.	

PRIMARY PRODUCTIVITY ○○○

As little as 1% of the sun's radiant light energy is converted to chemical energy by plants for distribution throughout the ecosystem, but this is sufficient to support all life on Earth.

Complete the equation.

net primary productivity (NPP) =

DON'T FORGET
NPP represents the storage of chemical energy to consumers in an ecosystem.

WATCH OUT
Don't confuse NPP with the total biomass of autotrophs present at a given time, called the standing crop biomass. Primary productivity is the *rate* at which the organism synthesizes *new* biomass.

THE JARGON
Trophic efficiency is the percentage of energy at one trophic level which is incorporated into the next trophic level.

TROPHIC EFFICIENCY AND ENERGY LOSS ○○○

In the secondary consumer illustrated more than half the food eaten passes straight through (figures show the energy flow in kJ/m²/y⁻¹).

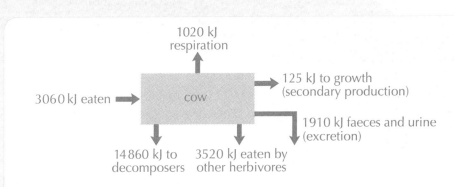

Use the information in the diagram to answer the question.

Calculate % excreted

(3060 − 1910 = 1150 is absorbed into the blood)

Calculate % respired

Calculate % in growth

So only about 10% of the absorbed energy is available to the next trophic level. How much energy is consumed by other organisms?

Why does a cow seem to eat all day long, whereas a lion eats about once a week?

Turn the page for some exam questions on this topic ➤

EXAM QUESTION 1 ●●●

The diagram shows what happens to food energy consumed by a sheep (all units are MJ/day^{-1}).

Have a go at answering a question about a sheep this time!

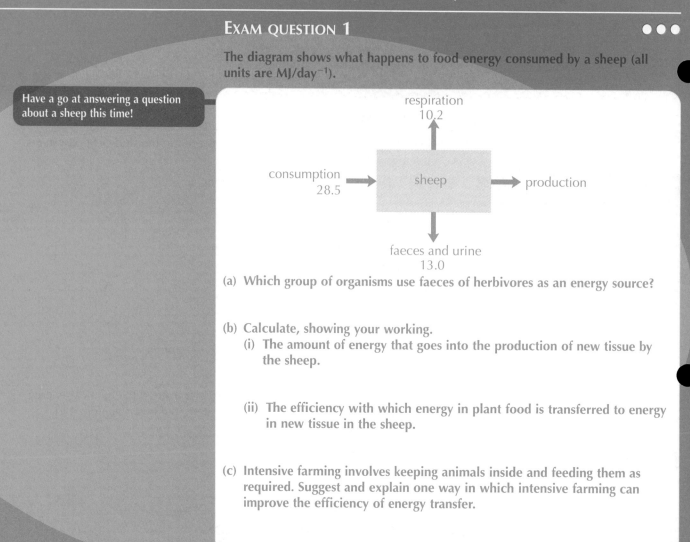

(a) Which group of organisms use faeces of herbivores as an energy source?

(b) Calculate, showing your working.
(i) The amount of energy that goes into the production of new tissue by the sheep.

(ii) The efficiency with which energy in plant food is transferred to energy in new tissue in the sheep.

(c) Intensive farming involves keeping animals inside and feeding them as required. Suggest and explain one way in which intensive farming can improve the efficiency of energy transfer.

EXAM QUESTION 2 ●●●

The table shows the flow of energy in a tropical forest.

This question is about an ecosystem.

Trophic level	Energy entering (kJ/m^2/y^{-1})
producers	200×10^3
primary consumers	6.7×10^3
secondary consumers	6.7×10^2
tertiary consumers	6.7×10^1
decomposers	23.6×10^3

(a) (i) If the producers lose 133×10^3 kJ/m^2/y^{-1} through respiration, what percentage of their stored energy is taken up by primary consumers?

(ii) Explain why the energy entering the decomposers is greater than that entering all the consumers.

(b) Predict one way in which the data for the tropical forest might differ from a forest ecosystem in Britain.

Food chains and food webs

Each ecosystem has a trophic structure of feeding relationships. Ecologists divide the organisms in a community or ecosystem into trophic levels on the basis of their main source of nutrition.

TROPHIC LEVELS AND FEEDING RELATIONSHIPS   OOO

These are some definitions of terms used in connection with feeding relationships.

Give the correct term for the definitions.

LINKS
An ecosystem's trophic structure determines the route of energy flow and nutrient cycling.
See pages 61 and 67.

DON'T FORGET
Natural feeding relationships are usually more like webs because some consumers feed at several different trophic levels.
Some autotrophs can also make organic molecules from the oxidation of inorganic molecules.

SYLLABUS CHECK
Some additional terms may be used in your syllabus.

IF YOU HAVE TIME
Make a list of all the organisms living in a habitat. Build up a food web by interconnecting all the organisms using arrows. Don't forget that the arrow heads indicate the direction of energy flow.

For the grassland habitat place the following organisms in the correct trophic level.
fungus, toad, stoat, snake, caterpillar, grass.

THE JARGON
Detritus is made up of non-living organic material, such as faeces, fallen leaves and the remains of dead organisms.

The pathway along which food is transferred from trophic level to trophic level, beginning with the primary producers.	
The elaborate, interconnected feeding relationships in an ecosystem.	
An organism that uses energy from the sun to make organic molecules from inorganic.	
An organism that obtains organic food molecules by eating other organisms or their by-products.	
An organism that acts as a decomposer by absorbing nutrients from dead organic matter.	
An organism that obtains nutrients from the body fluids of living hosts.	
An organism which feeds on small fragments of organic debris from decomposing plants and animals.	
Microbes that obtain nutrients from dead organisms, faeces etc. by extracellular digestion.	

Organisms in a habitat occupy a particular trophic level.

	producer
	primary consumer
	secondary consumer
	tertiary consumer
	quaternary consumer
	decomposer

DECOMPOSERS AND DETRITIVORES   OOO

Decomposition interconnects all trophic levels.

Insert the correct heading, decomposer or detritivore, at points A and B of the table.

DON'T FORGET
Decomposition accounts for most of the conversion of organic material from all trophic levels into inorganic compounds that are recycled.

	A	B
size	larger	microscopic
type of digestion	internal	external
example	earthworm	bacteria
food	small fragments of organic debris	faeces

Turn the page for some exam questions on this topic ➤

EXAM QUESTION 1 ●●●

The food web shows some of the feeding relationships of the peregrine falcon, a bird of prey which lives and nests on cliffs by the sea and feeds on other birds.

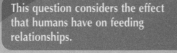

You may be required to predict the effect on food webs when an organism is removed or its numbers are increased. So try this question.

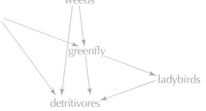

WATCH OUT
There could be an increase or decrease in numbers of the common tern. There could be an increase as fewer crustaceans are eaten, providing more food for small fish, which in turn would provide more food for the common tern. However, there could be a decrease since the peregrine falcon has only the common tern to feed on.

Answer questions (a) to (e) in the table.

(a) The ultimate source of energy for all the organisms.	
(b) A mammalian herbivore.	
(c) One organism which is a producer.	
(d) The effect on the common tern population if the numbers of common gulls were reduced.	
(e) The effect on the thrush population if the numbers of pigeons were increased.	

EXAM QUESTION 2 ●●●

The diagram shows a simple food web.

This question considers the effect that humans have on feeding relationships.

weeds
cereals
greenfly
ladybirds
detritivores

The table compares the effect of an insecticide, a selective herbicide (only kills weeds), and manure application on the biomass of each trophic level.

(a) Complete the table using one of the three following symbols to describe the change in *each* trophic level.

I = large increase; D = large decrease; O = no change

THE JARGON
Biomass means 'the dry weight of organic matter comprising a group of organisms in a particular habitat'.

EXAMINER'S SECRETS
Only one of these symbols should be placed in each box.

Treatment	Cereals	Weeds	Greenfly	Ladybirds
insecticide				
herbicide			O	O
manure				

(b) Name the organisms which represent the trophic level which shows the lowest energy content.

(c) Explain why this trophic level has the lowest energy content.

LINK
Look at pages 63–64 for more information.

Ecological pyramids

Within a community the food relationships and trophic levels can be shown by one or more ecological pyramids, as well as by food webs. The quantification of feeding relationships within a specific ecosystem involves obtaining numerical data.

THE THREE TYPES OF PYRAMIDS ○○○

The simplified diagrams show the three different ecological pyramids.

> Identify pyramids A, B and C.

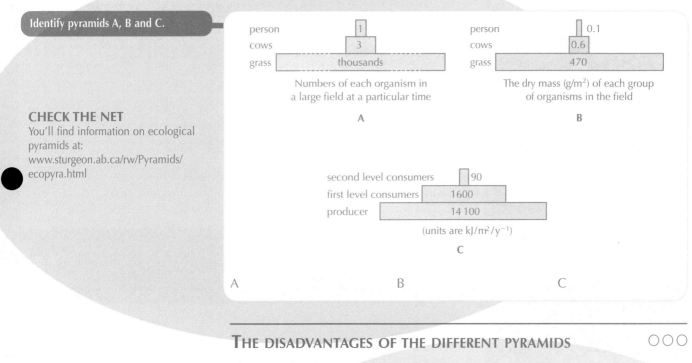

CHECK THE NET
You'll find information on ecological pyramids at:
www.sturgeon.ab.ca/rw/Pyramids/ecopyra.html

person	1
cows	3
grass	thousands

Numbers of each organism in a large field at a particular time

A

person	0.1
cows	0.6
grass	470

The dry mass (g/m²) of each group of organisms in the field

B

second level consumers	90
first level consumers	1600
producer	14 100

(units are kJ/m²/y⁻¹)

C

A   B   C

THE DISADVANTAGES OF THE DIFFERENT PYRAMIDS ○○○

There are disadvantages in using the different forms of pyramids.

> Describe the disadvantages of the different types of pyramids by putting the number of the statement which applies alongside the appropriate pyramid definition in the table below. (Some statements may be used more than once.)

1. It is difficult and laborious to obtain data.
2. Numbers of some individuals are so large it is impossible to represent them to scale.
3. Inverted pyramids can be created.
4. Organisms have to have their dry weight measured and this means destroying them.
5. All organisms are given the same value regardless of size.
6. No account is made for juvenile forms of a species whose diet and energy requirements may differ from the adult.
7. It is a snapshot view. This is called 'standing crop'.
8. Timing of taking the sample may affect the result and there is no indication of total productivity.
9. To measure the individuals a sample has to be taken and this may not be representative.
10. It is complex and difficult to obtain data.

THE JARGON
Standing crop describes the amount of living material present at a given instant in time.
The energy pyramid introduces a time factor and represents energy flow per unit time (say, one year). It therefore gives the best overall view of the community.
Units are kJ/m²/y⁻¹.

A pyramid of numbers is a bar diagram indicating the relative numbers of organisms at each trophic level in a food chain at any one time.	
A pyramid of biomass represents the total dry mass of organisms at each trophic level of a food chain at any one time.	
A pyramid of energy is a bar diagram drawn in proportion to the total energy utilized at each trophic level.	

Turn the page for some exam questions on this topic ➤

EXAM QUESTION 1   ● ● ●

A gardener was spraying a rose bush to try to get rid of the numerous greenfly which were feeding on the leaves and buds. He was helped by a few ladybirds. When he returned to his greenhouse he saw a blue tit eating some of the ladybirds.

Read the situation carefully before answering the question.

(a) Which one of the pyramids of numbers, A, B or C best represents the food chain described above?

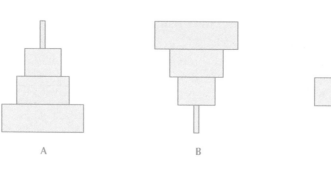

(b) Which shape would you expect for a pyramid of biomass for the same food chain?

EXAM QUESTION 2   ● ● ●

The diagram shows the pyramids of numbers and biomass in the same ecosystem.

Adapt some of the information on the previous page to answer this question.

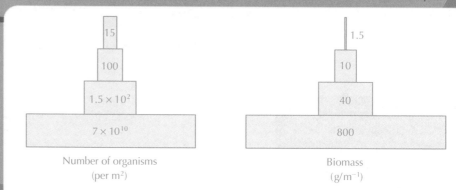

(a) What are the advantages and disadvantages of the two methods of measurement?

(b) Explain why some aquatic ecosystems have inverted biomass pyramids, with primary consumers outweighing producers.

THE JARGON
A short turnover time means a low standing crop biomass compared to the productivity.

(c) What other type of pyramid could provide further information about the four trophic levels?

Recycling of nutrients

Although ecosystems receive an inexhaustible influx of solar energy, chemical elements are available only in limited amounts. Life therefore depends on the recycling of essential chemical elements.

CHECK YOUR SYLLABUS
Leave out the carbon cycle if you're studying the OCR syllabus.

DON'T FORGET
The amount of carbon dioxide in the atmosphere varies slightly with the seasons and superimposed on this seasonal fluctuation is a continuing increase in the overall concentration of atmospheric CO_2 caused by the combustion of fossil fuels by humans.

WATCH OUT
Plants respire all the time just as animals do! During high light intensity the rate of photosynthesis is greater than the rate of respiration so the overall gas released is oxygen.

Insert the appropriate word from this list to describe the processes at work in A to D: decomposition, respiration, combustion, photosynthesis.

IF YOU HAVE TIME
If you're studying the WJEC syllabus write an account of the ways in which human activities affect the carbon and nitrogen cycles. These include eutrophication, the greenhouse effect and global warming. If you're studying the OCR syllabus confine your account to the nitrogen cycle.

Use the correct term that describes the microbial processes taking place in the nitrogen cycle.

DON'T FORGET
Nitrogen is found in all amino acids which make up proteins. Nitrogen is available to plants only in the form of ammonium (NH_4^+) and nitrate (NO_3^-) ions which are taken up by the roots.

SYLLABUS CHECK
WJEC do not require the specific names of microbes. OCR require the specific names of *Nitrosomonas*, *Nitrobacter* and *Rhizobium* only. Edexcel require all the specific names listed in the table.

Explain why farming practices such as ploughing and improving drainage help improve soils.

THE CARBON CYCLE

○○○

There is a balance between the removal of carbon dioxide from the air by the photosynthetic activity of green plants and its return as a result of the respiration of all organisms. The diagram shows a simplified version of the carbon cycle.

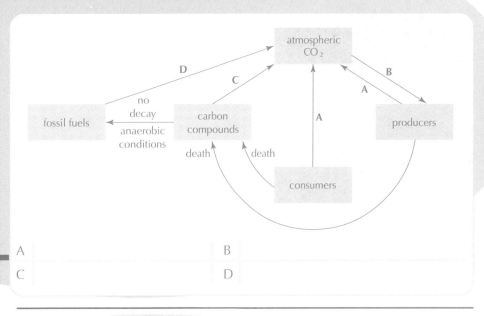

A		B	
C		D	

THE NITROGEN CYCLE

○○○

The following statements describe decay processes at work in the nitrogen cycle.

Process	Term	Microbe
the conversion of inorganic nitrogen into ammonia		aerobic bacteria and fungi
the conversion of ammonia into nitrites and then nitrates		*Nitrosomonas* *Nitrobacter* (aerobic)
the conversion of atmospheric nitrogen into nitrogen compounds		*Rhizobium* (symbiotic) *Azotobacter* (free-living)
the reduction of nitrates to molecular nitrogen		*Pseudomonas* *Thiobacillus* (anaerobic)

Turn the page for some exam questions on this topic ➤

EXAM QUESTION 1 ●●●

Indicate the one correct answer by writing the letter A, B, C, or D below.

The process which is common to both the carbon and nitrogen cycle is:

Try a multiple choice question.

A. combustion
B. decomposition
C. respiration
D. photosynthesis

EXAM QUESTION 2 ●●●

The diagram represents the nitrogen cycle.

This is a more demanding question on the nitrogen cycle.

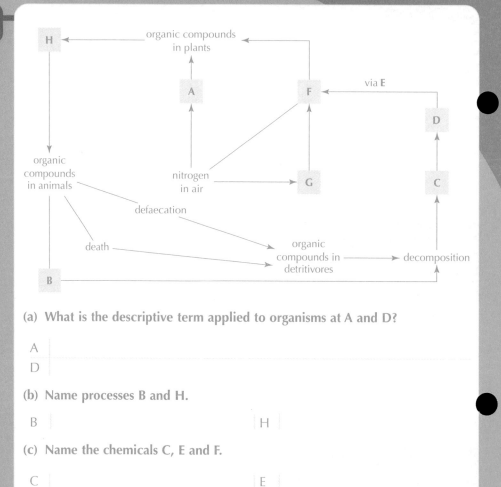

CHECK THE NET
You'll find information on how human activity is affecting nitrogen cycling at:
esa.sdsc.edu/tilman.htm
also at:
library.advanced.org/11353/text/nitrogen.htm

(a) What is the descriptive term applied to organisms at A and D?

A
D

(b) Name processes B and H.

B   H

(c) Name the chemicals C, E and F.

C   E
F

(d) Explain how growing leguminous plants such as clover, beans and peas at point A in a crop rotation scheme, could be used as a means of improving soil fertility.

(e) What could be produced by human means at point G?

Resource management and human influences

Humans are dependent on the Earth's resources for their survival. The increase in human population has meant that more food has to be produced to support it. In agriculture increased land use and the use of pesticides and fertilizers have improved crop yield. Environmental issues arise from their use.

RESOURCES ○○○

Renewable resources can be replaced whereas non-renewable resources cannot.

Tick the boxes to show whether the resources are renewable or not.

	Wood	Coal	Oil	Fish
renewable				
non-renewable				

MANAGEMENT ○○○

The list describes some of the ways of counteracting poor environmental management.

Suggest alternative resource management methods which may reduce the harmful effects.

insecticide resistance	
deforestation	
overfishing	
fossil fuel pollution	
eutrophication	

IF YOU HAVE TIME
This section needs careful consideration. Check your specification and devise your own revision cards.

THE JARGON
Lakes and rivers which suffer from eutrophication have little oxygen in the water.

HUMAN INFLUENCES ○○○

Humans can change the environment of crop plants.

Describe how these human activities can increase the yield of crops.

WATCH OUT
Don't simply state that yield is increased. Explain why.

using commercial glasshouses	
applying insecticides	
applying herbicides	
adding fertilizer	

Turn the page for some exam questions on this topic ➤

EXAM QUESTION 1 ● ● ●

Try out this question on deforestation.

SYLLABUS CHECK
This section should be checked carefully against your specification. Skip this question if you're doing the AQA(A) specification.

In the developing world the clearance of large tracts of forest (deforestation) to plant crops is becoming increasingly widespread. Diagram I shows the fate of rain falling on the natural vegetation on the steep sides of a valley. Diagram II shows the same slope cleared of trees and planted with maize. The solid and dotted arrows indicate the direction of flow and force of water.

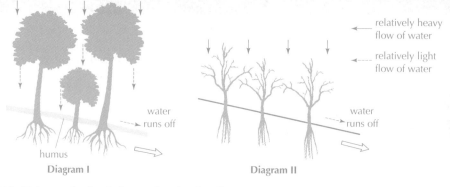

Diagram I   Diagram II

(a) Using only the information in the diagrams, suggest two different reasons why the force of the water running down the slope is less in diagram I than II.

EXAMINER'S SECRETS
The first part of the question asks for information provided in the question but for the rest of the question you should think back to your earlier work on ecology.

(b) Suggest a possible harmful consequence of the water run-off in diagram II to the people living in the valley.

(c) (i) Describe one possible long term effect of deforestation on the forest dwelling animals.

(ii) Suggest two possible explanations of the effect you have described.

EXAM QUESTION 2 ● ● ● ●

SYLLABUS CHECK
Skip this question if you're doing the Edexcel specification.

Pest control is best achieved using a combination of controls rather than biological or chemical controls alone.

These factors might be considered in an ideal answer.

Tick the boxes to show which method has the greater advantage for each of the factors listed.

Factors	Chemical	Biological
environmental contamination		
cost		
speed of effect		
application skill level		
specificity		
development of insect resistance		

THE JARGON
Specificity – a non-specific method kills beneficial as well as harmful organisms.

Using the information in the table discuss the relative advantages and disadvantages of biological and chemical contol.

A convincing argument might include the following.

EXAMINER'S SECRETS
Give definitions whenever possible. This shows the examiner that you have a good understanding of basic concepts.

Human reproduction

The control of the menstrual cycle is an excellent example of hormonal interaction.

THE JARGON
Primary oocytes are in the diploid state and each month after puberty one of these cells completes its development into an ovum (egg).

SYLLABUS CHECK
The Edexcel syllabus requires a knowledge of additional sub-topics.

LINK
For more information on meiotic cell division, see page 29.

THE OVARY AND OOGENESIS

○○○

The ovary consists of a number of oocytes at various stages of development. The diagram shows the various stages observed in an idealized section through a human ovary.

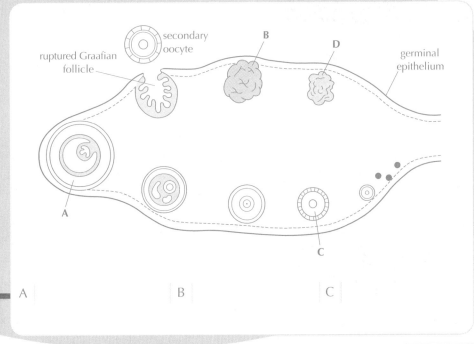

secondary oocyte

ruptured Graafian follicle

B

D

germinal epithelium

A

C

A	B	C

Name the stages labelled A, B and C and explain why B changes in appearance to become D.

IF YOU HAVE TIME
If you're studying the AQA(A) syllabus make a list of the ways in which reproduction can be manipulated and controlled in humans and domestic animals.

Tick the boxes to show the site of production of the hormones and show the order of their production by placing numbers 1 to 4 in the appropriate column.

DON'T FORGET
All four hormones are always present at some level but their levels fluctuate.

DON'T FORGET
The control of the menstrual cycle is an excellent example of hormone interaction, with an alternate switching on and off of the hormones. LH and FSH stimulate the ovaries to produce progesterone and oestrogen respectively.

Give the names of the hormones that carry out the functions listed.

WATCH OUT
This is a tricky topic. The study of graphs of the menstrual cycle will help your understanding.

HORMONAL CONTROL OF THE MENSTRUAL CYCLE

○○○

There are four hormones involved in the control of the female cycle and they are produced in a particular sequence.

Hormone	Gonadotrophic (pituitary)	Ovary	Order of production
oestrogen			
FSH			
progesterone			
LH			

The hormones have specific functions.

Causes Graafian follicles to develop in ovary. Stimulates ovary to produce oestrogen.
Inhibits the production and release of FSH. Causes regrowth of the uterus lining. Stimulates pituitary to produce LH.
Brings about ovulation. Stimulates ovary to produce oestrogen and progesterone from the corpus luteum.
Causes uterus lining to be maintained. Inhibits production of LH and FSH and stops further follicle development.

Turn the page for some exam questions on this topic ➤

EXAM QUESTION 1 ●●●

Fill in the missing words in the gaps in the following passage.

A high level of oestrogen indirectly stimulates ovulation in female mammals by causing the release of two hormones, ...A... and ...B.... The ...C... oocyte is released by the bursting of the ...D.... After release, the structure which remains in the ovary forms a solid mass called the ...E.... This structure secretes sufficient of the hormone ...F... to inhibit the production of ...G... by the ...H... gland. If fertilization occurs, it normally takes place in the ...I.... The fertilized zygote undergoes repeated division to form a hollow ball of cells called a ...J... and after 3–5 days ...K... occurs in the uterine endometrium.

Read the passage carefully before filling in the missing words.

A		B	
C		D	
E		F	
G		H	
I		J	
K			

EXAM QUESTION 2 ●●●

The diagram shows phases in the average menstrual cycle of 28 days. Indicate by writing the appropriate letter, the phase in which you would expect *each* of the following events:

Place the appropriate letters in the boxes.

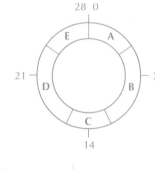

maximum secretion of LH	
menstruation	
fertilization	
implantation of the fertilized egg	

EXAM QUESTION 3 ●●●

Complete the table to show the correct function(s) of luteinizing hormone (LH), oestrogen and progesterone.

Tick the box or boxes to give the functions of the hormones. Take care, some hormones may have more than one function.

Function	LH	Oestrogen	Progesterone
immediate cause of ovulation			
immediate cause of regrowth of the uterine lining after menstruation			
inhibits production of FSH			
maintains the uterus for implantation			
stimulates the formation of a structure which produces progesterone			

Answer section

SEE HOW YOU GOT ON BY CHECKING AGAINST
THE ANSWERS GIVEN HERE.

Have you remembered to fill in the self-check
circles? Do this to track your progress.

For more detail on the topics covered in this book,
you can check the *Revision Express A-level Study
Guide,* your class notes or your own textbook.
You can also find exam questions and model
answers at www.revision-express.com.

Don't forget, tear out these answers and put
them in your folder for handy revision reference!

Carbohydrates and fats

Large molecules are made up of smaller building blocks. Carbohydrates and fats both contain carbon, hydrogen and oxygen but the elements are arranged differently in the molecules. Their properties and roles or functions in the organism differ.

CARBOHYDRATES

Carbohydrates include monosaccharides (single-sugars), disaccharides (double-sugars) and polysaccharides (many-sugars).

State whether the carbohydrates are mono-, di- or polysaccharides and give their function, stating if they occur in plants or animals or both.

Carbohydrate	Group	Role	Plant or animal
glucose	monosaccharide	energy	both
lactose	disaccharide	energy	animal
cellulose	polysaccharide	cell walls	plant
glycogen	polysaccharide	energy store	animal

WATCH OUT
Make sure you know the difference between a reducing and non-reducing sugar and the appropriate food test.

When two monosaccharides join together to form a disaccharide a molecule of water is released.

What term is given for this type of reaction and what type of bond is formed between the two molecules?

condensation reaction	glycosidic bond or link

Polysaccharides have different roles in living organisms.

Give the role of each polysaccharide and explain how their general structure is suited to their function.

Starch and glycogen.
Storage-glucose can be added or removed easily. They are insoluble and do not diffuse easily out of the cell. They have a compact shape.

Cellulose.
Structural – being made up of β-glucose units, with adjacent glucose molecules rotated by 180°, allows hydrogen bonds to be formed between adjacent parallel chains (forming microfibrils).

DON'T FORGET
In the ring structure form glucose can exist as α or β isomers. Starch is made up of α-glucose units, whereas cellulose is made up of β-glucose units.

FATS OR LIPIDS

A fat is made up of two different smaller molecules:

Complete the equation.

$$\text{glycerol} + 3 \text{ fatty acids} \quad = \quad \text{triglyceride} + \text{water}$$

Fats perform a variety of functions in both plants and animals:

List the main functions of fats with an example of where they may be found in each case.

Function	Example
energy store (energy source on breakdown)	muscle, seeds*
insulation	beneath dermis in skin
protection	around organs
constituent of phospholipids	cell membrane

DON'T FORGET
One gram of fat yields approximately twice as much energy as one gram of carbohydrate.

Turn the page for some exam questions on this topic ▶

For more on this topic, see pages 4-6 of the *Revision Express A-level Study Guide*

EXAM QUESTION 1

The table compares the properties of organic compounds. If the property is a characteristic feature of the compound mark the appropriate box or boxes with a tick (✓).

Have a go at ticking the boxes. Make sure you consider each box carefully. Each row should have one or more boxes ticked.

Property	Maltose	Sucrose	Starch	Lipid
a source of energy	✓	✓	✓	✓
a polysaccharide			✓	
produces monosaccharides on complete hydrolysis	✓	✓	✓	
soluble in water	✓	✓		
a reducing sugar	✓			
a main food store in some seeds			✓	✓

EXAMINER'S SECRETS
In this type of question one mark is given for each horizontal row that is completely correct. However, don't tick more boxes than is necessary or you will be penalized for this.

EXAM QUESTION 2

(a) Simple carbohydrate molecules can be written as $(CH_2O)n$. What is the name given to carbohydrates in which n is

(i)   6   *hexose*
(ii) 5   *pentose*
(iii) 3   *triose*

(b) Simple carbohydrates can be combined to form disaccharides and polysaccharides. What else is produced in these reactions?

water

(c) (i) Name the reagent used to test for the presence of reducing sugars in food.

Benedict's reagent

(ii) Name a sugar which would *not* give a positive test with this reagent.

sucrose

DON'T FORGET
Practical food tests and their details.

EXAM QUESTION 3

In living organisms small molecules are often built into large molecules, often with hundreds of small units repeated. The diagram shows the structural formulae of two such small molecules.

EXAMINER'S SECRETS
You should be able to recognize and use structural formulae e.g. glucose, amino acid, fatty acid, glycerol.

Complete the table.

Small molecule	Name or general name of molecule	General name of a class of large molecules which contains this small molecule
A	glycerol	lipid/triglyceride
B	glucose	carbohydrate

Proteins

There are relatively few carbohydrates and fats but there are a large number of proteins. There are approximately 800 different proteins in a typical bacterium and over 10 000 different proteins in humans! Nevertheless all proteins are polymers constructed from the same set of amino acids.

STRUCTURE

Amino acids differ according to their side chain or R group. Diagram A shows the general formula of an amino acid and diagram B shows the formula of one of the 20 amino acids.

| | amino group end | carboxyl group end |
| A | | B |

R group	Name of amino acid
H	glycine
CH$_3$	alanine
CH$_2$OH	serine

These phrases describe terms used in protein structure:

a reaction where a molecule of water is removed	condensation
the type of bond formed when two amino acids join	dipeptide
a long chain of amino acids	polypeptide

LEVELS OF PROTEIN STRUCTURE

When a cell synthesizes a polypeptide the chain coils and folds spontaneously, forming a functional protein of specific conformation.
The level of protein structure describes the degree of folding and is determined by the number and types of bonds formed.

Level of structure	Peptide	Hydrogen	Disulphide	Ionic
primary	✓			
secondary	✓	✓		
tertiary	✓	✓	✓	✓

CLASSIFICATION

Proteins can be classified according to function which is determined by structure.

insulin	globular
collagen	fibrous
lysozyme (an enzyme)	globular
keratin	fibrous

Turn the page for some exam questions on this topic ▶

THE JARGON
A polymer is a large molecule consisting of many identical or similar building blocks (monomers) linked by bonds, just like a train consists of a chain of carriages.

EXAMINER'S SECRETS
You are not expected to recall names of amino acids.

Construct a dipeptide from the diagram. With a coloured pen circle the lower –OH group of diagram A and the lower –H group of diagram B in order to 'remove' the molecule of water formed. Now join together the carbon, to which the –OH was attached, with the nitrogen to which the –H was attached.

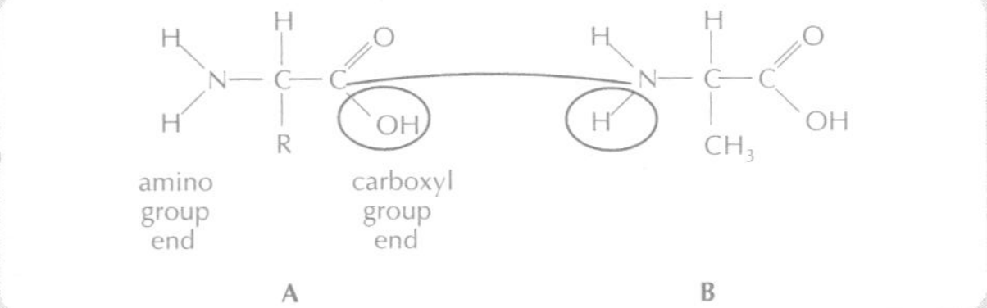

Use the information in the table to identify amino acid B and write your answer in the box.

Write an appropriate word alongside each phrase.

WATCH OUT
Take care how you spell protein.

Tick the boxes to show which bonds are present at each level of protein structure.

Classify the examples of proteins as either globular or fibrous.

For more on this topic, see pages 6–7 of the *Revision Express A-level Study Guide*

EXAM QUESTION 1

The diagram shows the structural formula of a molecule of a typical amino acid.

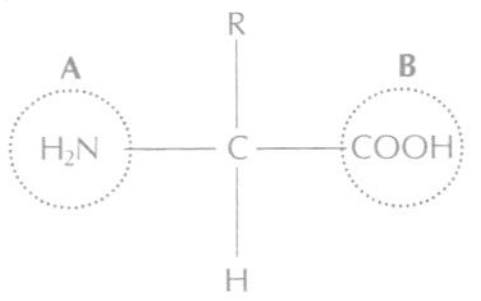

(a) Name the parts of the molecule labelled A and B.

A amino group

B carboxyl group

(b) State what R would represent in the simplest amino acid.

H/hydrogen

Try this simple question to begin with.

EXAM QUESTION 2

The diagram shows part of a protein molecule.

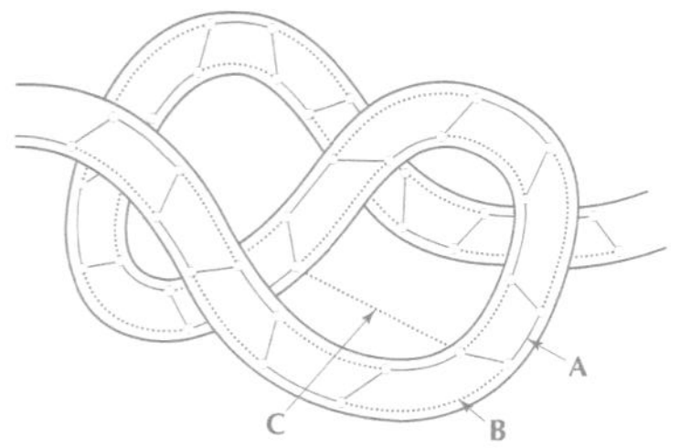

This question requires you to consider the diagram carefully.

(a) Name the level of protein structure which is shown.

tertiary structure or globular protein

(b) Suggest a function that such a structure might perform in the body.

enzyme/antibody/hormone/membrane carrier

(c) Explain what structural feature allows the performance of this function.

The formation of a specific shape with which the protein can bind with the complementary molecule, e.g. enzymes have an active site which allows the substrates to fit into.

(d) Name the bonds labelled

A peptide

B hydrogen

(e) Name one other type of bond which might form the bond labelled as C.

disulphide or ionic

EXAMINER'S SECRETS
Always study carefully the information provided in the question. It is there to help you and you are expected to use the information in your answer.

LINKS
For more information on enzymes, see page 15.

EXAMINER'S SECRETS
There are several possible correct answers in part (b). Write your explanation as concisely as possible to follow on logically from your answer.

Nucleic acids

Nucleic acids store and transmit hereditary information. DNA is unique among molecules in that it provides directions for making copies of itself and also directs RNA synthesis and, through RNA, controls protein synthesis.

CHECK THE NET
You'll learn more about nucleic acids at www.biology.arizona.edu/molecular_bio/problem_sets/nucleic_nucleic_acids_1.shtm

NUCLEOTIDE STRUCTURE
Nucleotides are the sub-units of nucleic acids. They are formed by condensation reactions when three components combine:

DON'T FORGET
Nucleic acids are polynucleotides with the phosphate group forming a bridge between one sugar molecule and the next by means of a condensation reaction. The bases form the 'rungs' of the 'ladder' and the alternating phosphate and sugar groups form the 'uprights'.

Name the parts of the structure of a typical nucleotide.

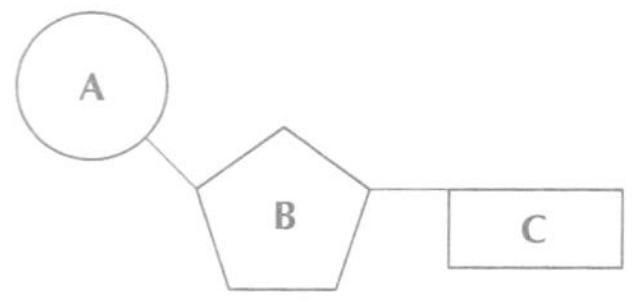

A .... phosphate
B .... sugar
C .... base

Organic bases are divided into two groups.

Name of group	Single or double rings	Names of bases
pyrimidines	single	cytosine, thymine, uracil
purines	double	adenine, guanine

Complete the table that describes the organic bases.

DEOXYRIBONUCLEIC ACID – DNA
Two polynucleotide chains are held together by hydrogen bonds. The greatest number of hydrogen bonds is formed when purines pair with pyrimidines.

adenine pairs with thymine
guanine pairs with cytosine

What are the complementary base pairs in DNA?

RIBONUCLEIC ACID–RNA
ribosomal RNA, transfer RNA, messenger RNA

EXAMINER'S SECRETS
Questions are often asked about the stability of DNA. You may be expected to explain how this stability is achieved by complementary base pairs.

List the three types of RNA.

DIFFERENCES BETWEEN DNA AND RNA

	DNA	RNA
single or double chain	double	single
type of sugar	deoxyribose	ribose
bases (as abbreviations)	A, G, C, T	A, G, C, U
helix type	double	single
location	nucleus	throughout cell

Complete the table to show some of the differences between DNA and RNA.

WATCH OUT
In RNA adenine pairs with uracil.

Turn the page for some exam questions on this topic ►

For more on this topic, see pages 8–9 of the *Revision Express A-level Study Guide*

EXAM QUESTION 1
The diagram represents the molecular structure of part of a DNA molecule.

Attempt this question on DNA.

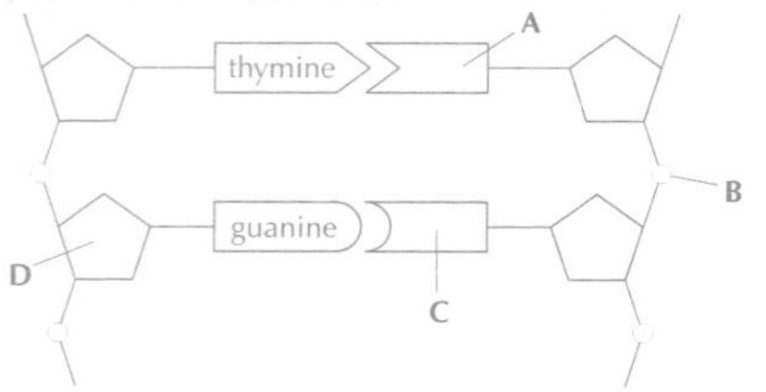

(a) Name the parts A–D.
A .... adenine
B .... phosphate
C .... cytosine
D .... deoxyribose

(b) Explain why DNA needs to be a very stable molecule.
Stability is an essential feature of a molecule which is passed from generation to generation over millions of years. If it were altered imperfect copies would be made.

(c) Part of a DNA molecule has the following sequence of bases.
Write the sequence of bases of the complementary portion of DNA.

DNA molecule	T	A	T	C	G
complementary DNA	A	T	A	G	C

(d) Biochemical analysis of a sample of DNA showed that 30% of the bases were guanine. Calculate the percentage of the bases in the sample which would be adenine. Show how you arrived at your answer.

Since guanine pairs with cytosine this must also make up 30% of the bases. Guanine + cytosine equals 60%. The other two bases must together make up 40%. As these two bases are also equal in amount adenine must make up 20%.

EXAMINER'S SECRETS
Always show your working. Examiners know that the answer appears on the calculator screen. They also need to know how that answer was achieved.

EXAM QUESTION 2
The table compares DNA and RNA.

Tick the boxes to show the differences and similarities between DNA and RNA.

	DNA	RNA
contains ribose		✓
contains uracil		✓
contains adenine	✓	✓
double chain	✓	
exists as one form	✓	

Replication

During DNA replication, base pairing enables existing DNA strands to act as templates for new complementary strands.

HOW REPLICATION TAKES PLACE – SEMI-CONSERVATIVE MODEL ○○○

A parent molecule has two complementary strands of DNA which unwind into two separate strands.

THE JARGON
Another word for template is blueprint.

Use a coloured pen to complete the diagrams.

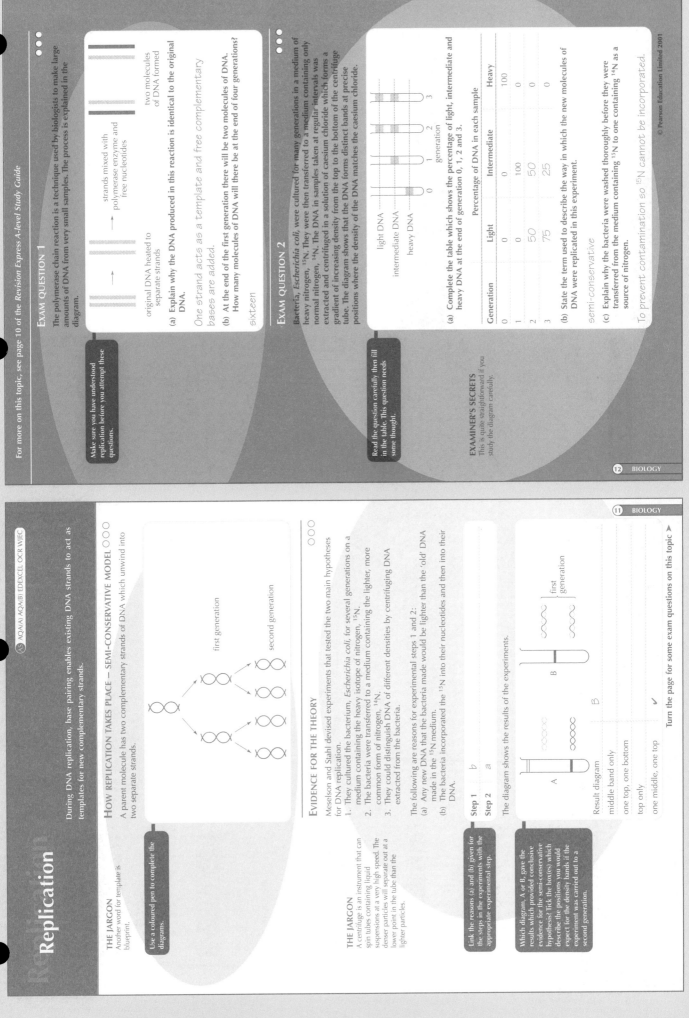

first generation

second generation

EVIDENCE FOR THE THEORY ○○○

Meselson and Stahl devised experiments that tested the two main hypotheses for DNA replication.

1. They cultured the bacterium, *Escherichia coli*, for several generations on a medium containing the heavy isotope of nitrogen, ^{15}N.
2. The bacteria were transferred to a medium containing the lighter, more common form of nitrogen, ^{14}N.
3. They could distinguish DNA of different densities by centrifuging DNA extracted from the bacteria.

THE JARGON
A centrifuge is an instrument that can spin tubes containing liquid suspensions at a very high speed. The denser particles will separate out at a lower point in the tube than the lighter particles.

The following are reasons for experimental steps 1 and 2:
(a) Any new DNA that the bacteria made would be lighter than the 'old' DNA made in the ^{15}N medium.
(b) The bacteria incorporated the ^{15}N into their nucleotides and then into their DNA.

Link the reasons (a) and (b) given for the steps in the experiments with the appropriate experimental step.

Step 1   *b*

Step 2   *a*

The diagram shows the results of the experiments.

Which diagram, A or B, gave the results which provided conclusive evidence for the semi-conservative hypothesis? Tick the box(es) which describe the positions you would expect for the density bands if the experiment was carried out to a second generation.

Result diagram   *B*

middle band only

one top, one bottom

top only

one middle, one top   ✓

Turn the page for some exam questions on this topic ▶

For more on this topic, see page 10 of the *Revision Express A-level Study Guide*

EXAM QUESTION 1

The polymerase chain reaction is a technique used by biologists to make large amounts of DNA from very small samples. The process is explained in the diagram.

Make sure you have understood replication before you attempt these questions.

original DNA heated to separate strands → strands mixed with polymerase enzyme and free nucleotides → two molecules of DNA formed

(a) Explain why the DNA produced in this reaction is identical to the original DNA.

One strand acts as a template and free complementary bases are added.

(b) At the end of the first generation there will be two molecules of DNA. How many molecules of DNA will there be at the end of four generations?

sixteen

EXAM QUESTION 2

Bacteria, *Escherichia coli*, were cultured for many generations in a medium of heavy nitrogen, ^{15}N. They were then transferred to a medium containing only normal nitrogen, ^{14}N. The DNA in samples taken at regular intervals was extracted and centrifuged in a solution of caesium chloride which forms a gradient of increasing density from the top to the bottom of the centrifuge tube. The diagram shows that the DNA forms distinct bands at precise positions where the density of the DNA matches the caesium chloride.

Read the question carefully then fill in the table. This question needs some thought.

light DNA
intermediate DNA
heavy DNA

generation   0   1   2   3

(a) Complete the table which shows the percentage of light, intermediate and heavy DNA at the end of generation 0, 1, 2 and 3.

Generation	Percentage of DNA in each sample		
	Light	Intermediate	Heavy
0	0	0	100
1	0	100	0
2	50	50	0
3	75	25	0

(b) State the term used to describe the way in which the new molecules of DNA were replicated in this experiment.

semi-conservative

EXAMINER'S SECRETS
This is quite straightforward if you study the diagram carefully.

(c) Explain why the bacteria were washed thoroughly before they were transferred from the medium containing ^{15}N to one containing ^{14}N as a source of nitrogen.

To prevent contamination so ^{15}N cannot be incorporated.

Protein synthesis

AS AQA(A) AQA(B) EDEXCEL OCR WJEC

The information content of DNA, the genetic material, is in the form of specific sequences of nucleotides along the DNA strands. A gene is a DNA sequence coding for a specific polypeptide chain.

THE NATURE OF THE GENETIC CODE ○○○

How can only four nucleotides produce 20 different amino acids?
If each nucleotide coded for one amino acid it would be possible to make four amino acids.
What would happen if the code consisted of pairs of nucleotides?

> Fill in the boxes in the table, with all the possible permutations of bases in pairs.

	A	T	G	C
A	AA	AT	AG	AC
T	TA	TT	TG	TC
G	GA	GT	GG	GC
C	CA	CT	CG	CC

> Complete the boxes.

Type of code (codon)	Formula	Possible number of amino acids
code in nucleotide pairs	4^2	16
code in nucleotide triplets	4^3	64

These terms describe the code:

> Explain concisely the meaning of the terms.

non-overlapping	each triplet is read separately
universal	same in all organisms
degenerate	more than one triplet for each amino acid
stop or nonsense	act as termination signals

STAGES IN PROTEIN SYNTHESIS ○○○

There are three stages in protein synthesis – transcription, amino acid activation, translation.

> Write one word or phrase next to the appropriate definition.

The synthesis of mRNA from DNA code directed by RNA polymerase	transcription
The combination of amino acids with tRNA using energy from ATP	amino acid activation
The synthesis by the ribosome of a polypeptide under the direction of mRNA	translation

The translation process:

> The table lists two amino acids and the base sequences on a DNA strand which code for them in protein synthesis. It will help you to arrive at your answer if you first complete the boxes. This is quite tricky!

Amino acid	DNA triplet code	mRNA codon	tRNA anticodon
glycine	CCT	GGA	CCT
methionine	TAC	AUG	UAC

If a tRNA molecule had an anticodon UAC, name the amino acid carried by this molecule. **methionine**

> **IF YOU HAVE TIME**
> Write out a step by step account of protein synthesis using the three stages opposite as headings.

> **WATCH OUT**
> In RNA uracil replaces thymine, so A pairs with U.

Turn the page for some exam questions on this topic ▶

For more on this topic, see pages 10–11 of the *Revision Express A-level Study Guide*

EXAM QUESTION 1

(a) The table shows the functions of DNA, messenger RNA (mRNA) and transfer RNA (tRNA).

> Where the statement applies mark the appropriate box with a tick.

Statement	DNA	mRNA	tRNA
site of codon		✓	
site of anticodon			✓
attaches to ribosome		✓	✓
translated		✓	
carries amino acid to ribosome			✓
transcribed but not translated	✓		

> **EXAMINER'S SECRETS**
> In this question only one tick per horizontal row is required

(b) The number of bases in a gene coding for a polypeptide is 642. Estimate the number of amino acids in the polypeptide chain.

Since three bases code for one amino acid, 642/3 = 214.

> **WATCH OUT**
> Make sure you explain how you arrived at your answer.

EXAM QUESTION 2

The diagram shows part of the sequence of events which take place when a protein is synthesized.

> Try this question which tests one particular aspect of protein synthesis.

(a) Name:
the step in protein synthesis shown	translation
the cell organelle where these events take place	ribosome/rough ER
feature X	peptide bond
feature Y	codon
feature Z	amino acid

(b) State the base sequence on molecules L and M.
L   AUG
M   GCU

(c) Describe fully what happens after the amino acid has been linked in the above process.

The tRNA which carried it to the mRNA is released back into the cytoplasm and is again free to combine with another specific amino acid. The ribosome continues along the mRNA until each amino acid is linked and a 'nonsense' code is reached.

> **EXAMINER'S SECRETS**
> Be prepared to answer questions on one particular aspect of protein synthesis. Only an essay question can test your knowledge of the whole process.

© Pearson Education Limited 2001

For more on this topic, see pages 12–13 of the *Revision Express A-level Study Guide*

Enzymes

AS AQA(A) AQA(B) EDEXCEL OCR WJEC

Without enzymes, chemical reactions that occur in living organisms would take place very slowly and in an uncontrolled way.

PROPERTIES OF ENZYMES

Here are some key terms:

catalyst biological	Alters the rate of a chemical reaction without itself being changed.
activation energy lowers	The energy which must be applied before a chemical reaction can get underway.
active site	A region on the enzyme to which the substrate binds.
lock and key specific	Most enzymes work on only one particular substrate.
lock and key	When the three-dimensional shape of the enzyme molecule is altered to such an extent that the active site no longer fits the substrate.
denature temperature	

Each of the following words or phrases can be applied to one or more of the terms above:

lowers; lock and key; temperature; biological.

Write a concise definition for each term.

DON'T FORGET
The specificity of an enzyme is attributed to a comparable fit between the shape of its active site and the shape of the substrate. To help understanding, the process is sometimes referred to as a lock and key mechanism.

WATCH OUT
Enzymes are destroyed by high temperatures but work very slowly at 0°C.

Write the most appropriate word or phrase beneath each of the key terms above.

HOW ENZYMES WORK

Enzyme + substrate → enzyme–substrate complex → enzyme + product

Complete the equation.

IF YOU HAVE TIME
Study the 'lock and key' mechanism and consider the 'induced fit' theory.

FACTORS AFFECTING ENZYME ACTION

The speed at which an enzyme works can be affected by factors.

Temperature, pH, concentration (conc.) of substrate, concentration of enzyme.

Apart from inhibition, list four factors that affect enzyme action. Label the horizontal axis of each graph with the appropriate factor.

Rate of reaction — Temperature

Rate of reaction — Substrate conc.

Rate of reaction — pH

DON'T FORGET
Describe enzyme and substrate action in terms of molecular collisions. As temperature increases the kinetic energy of the molecules increases.

Turn the page for some exam questions on this topic ▶

EXAM QUESTION 1

The enzyme sucrase breaks down the disaccharide sucrose to glucose and fructose. Sucrase has no effect on other disaccharides such as lactose or maltose.

With reference to their molecular structure, explain why enzymes such as sucrase can break down some compounds but not others.

Each enzyme exists as a three-dimensional structure, with the active site being made up of only a few catalytic amino acids folded in such a way that it has a specific shape, so that only those substrate molecules with a complementary shape will combine with the enzyme.

Try this question which is about enzyme specificity.

LINKS
For more information on protein structure, see page 7.

EXAMINER'S SECRETS
You could also gain marks by referring to the formation of an enzyme-substrate complex and the 'lock and key'/induced fit hypotheses.

EXAM QUESTION 2

An enzyme extract from a plant was mixed with substrate and the rate of reaction measured at different temperatures. The results are plotted in the graph below.

Rate of reaction (arbitrary units) vs Temperature (°C)

(a) What is the approximate optimum temperature for this enzyme supported by the evidence, and how could this have been more precisely determined?

Between 30°C and 50°C. Repeat the experiment at say 2°C intervals close to the optimum.

(b) Explain the increase in the rate of reaction between 0°C and 30°C.

As the temperature increases, the kinetic energy of the enzyme and substrate molecules increases, so there are more collisions and so more enzyme–substrate complexes are formed.

(c) Explain the decrease in the rate of reaction between 40°C and 60°C.

With increase in temperature above the optimum, hydrogen bonds, which hold the enzyme molecules in their precise shape, are broken. The three-dimensional shape of the enzyme molecules is altered to such an extent that their active sites no longer fit the substrate. The enzyme is said to be denatured.

Study the graph, then answer the question.

EXAMINER'S SECRETS
You are expected to deduce from the graph that the experiment has been carried out at 10°C intervals. The optimum could be lower or greater than 40°C.

DON'T FORGET
Remember to link your practical work to your theory answers.

Enzyme inhibition

AS AQA(A) AQA(B) EDEXCEL OCR WJEC

Inhibition occurs when enzyme action is slowed down or stopped by another substance. Certain chemicals selectively inhibit the action of specific enzymes, allowing a cell to regulate its metabolic pathways by controlling where and when its various enzymes are active.

COMPETITIVE AND NON-COMPETITIVE INHIBITION   ○○○

These reversible inhibitors are of two types:

Features of inhibitor	Competitive	Non-competitive
changes shape of active site	no	yes
binds to active site	yes	no
similar in structure to substrate	yes	no
malonic acid inhibitor	yes	no
affected by concentration of substrate	yes	no
cyanide inhibitor	no	yes

Describe the inhibitors by answering *yes* **or** *no* **opposite each statement.**

DON'T FORGET
Sketches and graphs will help you understand the differences between the different types of inhibitors.

EXAMINER'S SECRETS
Describe enzyme–substrate reaction in terms of molecular collisions. With competitive inhibition the greater the substrate concentration in relation to the inhibitor, the greater the *chance* that the substrate will collide with the enzyme.

Competitive and non-competitive inhibitors react differently to an increase in substrate concentration.

The graph shows how the reaction proceeds normally and in the presence of inhibitors.

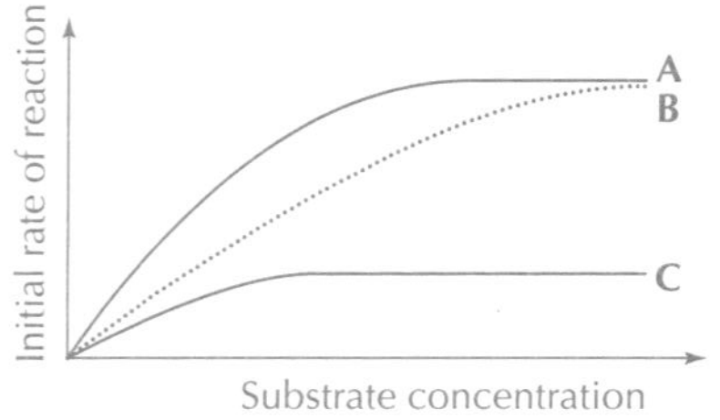

Graph: Initial rate of reaction (y-axis) against Substrate concentration (x-axis), showing curves A, B and C.

No inhibitor	A At low concentrations the substrate is the limiting factor but at high substrate concentrations a point is reached when all active sites are occupied. A maximum rate is reached and the curve levels off.
Competitive inhibitor	B As the substrate concentration increases there is an increased chance of the substrate and enzyme meeting (rather than inhibitor and enzyme).
Non-competitive inhibitor	C The enzyme is inactivated, but as inhibitor does not enter the active site the reaction is independent of substrate concentration.

In the table label the three lines which appear in the graph. Explain the difference between the shapes of lines A, B and C.

DON'T FORGET
As the graph shows, the same amount of product is formed with a competitive inhibitor but it takes *longer* to make the products.

DON'T FORGET
Both competitive and non-competitive inhibition are reversible.

Turn the page for some exam questions on this topic ▶

For more on this topic, see pages 14–15 of the *Revision Express A-level Study Guide*

EXAM QUESTION 1   •••

(a) Explain what is meant by the term 'competitive enzyme inhibitor'.

A molecule which has a similar shape to an enzyme's normal substrate and fits into the enzyme's active site (changing its shape), blocking the formation of an enzyme–substrate complex.

(b) A mixture is prepared containing an enzyme, a competitive inhibitor and a small amount of substrate.

(i) What would be the probable effect on the rate of reaction if more substrate is added?

The rate of formation of product would increase.

(ii) Explain your answer.

The chance of an enzyme–substrate molecular contact is now greater than the chance of an enzyme–inhibitor contact.

Try this straightforward recall question.

EXAMINER'S SECRETS
Note the amount of detail expected in an answer at this level.

EXAM QUESTION 2   •••

An enzyme catalyses the reaction between substrates A and B. Molecule C acts as an inhibitor in the reaction.

Diagram: enzyme, substrate A, substrate B, inhibitor C.

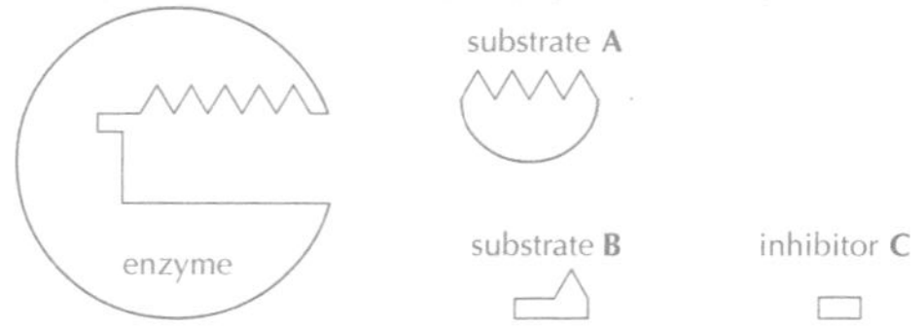

(a) Using the information in the diagram suggest an explanation for this inhibition.

C competes with B since it has a similar shape and blocks the substrate from entering the active site. C acts as a competitive inhibitor.

(b) The diagram below shows a reaction sequence with the production of an end product.

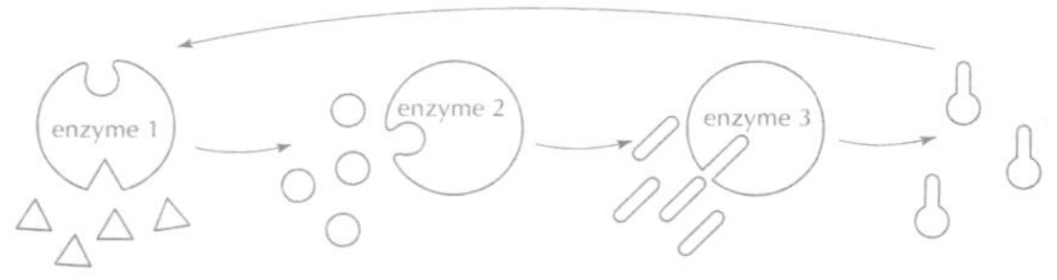

Diagram: enzyme 1, enzyme 2, enzyme 3, substrates → substrates → substrates → product.

When sufficient product has been made how is the reaction stopped?

The product shape attaches to enzyme 1 at a point other than the active site and acts as a non-competitive inhibitor (this prevents the accumulation of unnecessary intermediates).

This question requires a little more thought but should pose little problem if you use the information provided in the diagrams.

SYLLABUS CHECK
Skip part (b) if it's not on your syllabus.

© Pearson Education Limited 2001

Enzyme applications

AS AQA(A) EDEXCEL WJEC

The ability of enzymes to perform as catalysts when isolated from cells has led to their use in industrial processes. Enzymes also have analytical uses in medicine.

COMMERCIAL USES OF ENZYMES

The table describes some applications of enzymes:

Application	Enzymes used	Uses
'biological' detergents	protease	in pre-soak and main wash to remove protein e.g. blood stains
dairy industry	lactose	breaks down lactose to glucose and galactose
food industry	pectinase	clearing of wines and fruit juices

Complete the table by naming the enzymes involved.

IMMOBILIZED ENZYMES

Advantages to using immobilized enzymes instead of 'free' enzymes are as follows:

• Structure is stabilized with an inert insoluble polymer.
• Easily recovered for reuse, reducing overall costs.
• Enzyme can tolerate a wider range of conditions/several enzymes with differing pH or temperature optima can be used together.

List two advantages of immobilized enzymes.

THE JARGON
'Inert' means 'chemically unreactive'.

THE JARGON
The term 'biosensor' describes the association of a biomolecule, such as an enzyme, with a transducer which produces an electrical signal in response to substrate transformation. The strength of the electrical signal may be measured with a suitable meter.

BIOSENSORS

The diagram shows a simplified version of a glucose oxidase biosensor used to detect glucose in blood.

product
oxygen glucose
O_2
membrane
anode
cathode
enzyme gel layer (immobilized enzyme)

1. Oxygen is taken up.
2. A digital display shows an accurate concentration of glucose.
3. Blood contains a mixture of different molecules.
4. Enzyme electrode is placed in blood sample.
5. The rate of oxygen uptake is proportional to the glucose concentration.
6. Glucose diffuses into the immobilized enzyme layer.

3-4-6-1-5-2

SYLLABUS CHECK
Skip biosensors if you're doing the Edexcel syllabus.

Sentences 1 to 6 describe how a biosensor is used. But they are in the wrong order! Put them in the correct order starting with sentence number 3.

Turn the page for some exam questions on this topic ▶

For more on this topic, see page 13 of the *Revision Express A-level Study Guide*

EXAM QUESTION 1

Enzymes are difficult to recover at the end of an industrial process. However, enzymes are easily reused if they are immobilized. The graph shows the effect of temperature on the maximum rate of reaction with an enzyme in its free state and in its immobilized state.

Have a go at interpreting the graph and diagram in this question.

(a) Describe four differences between the effects of temperature on the immobilized and the 'free' enzyme.

With the immobilized enzyme:
• there is a larger increase in the rate of reaction between 0°C and 30°C
• optimum temperature covers a wider range
• above 40°C it is more reactive/more active at all temperatures except 40°C
• denatured at a higher temperature.

(b) Suggest how trapping and holding an enzyme in a framework of cellulose microfibrils, as shown in the simplified diagram below, can explain the differences you have described in (a).

substrate
cellulose microfibrils
enzyme
covalent bonds
product

The shape (3-D) of the enzyme is maintained. The enzyme is stabilized and can't move.

EXAM QUESTION 2

(a) State a clinical use of biosensors.

The quantitative detection of urea or glucose in blood.

(b) From your knowledge of enzymes, suggest how chemical reactions giving large temperature changes would be unsuitable for measurement by biosensors.

The enzyme used would be denatured.

(c) Suggest two advantages of using a biosensor rather than a chemical test such as Benedict's test to determine the amount of glucose in a test sample.

More sensitive – smaller concentrations can be detected.
More accurate.

EXAMINER'S SECRETS
An increase in temperature causes an increased movement of molecules. Violent molecular movement results in bonds being broken, resulting in denaturation.

SYLLABUS CHECK
Skip this question if you're doing the Edexcel syllabus.

Cell structure

Every organism is composed of one of two structurally different types of cells: prokaryotic cells or eukaryotic cells. Eukaryotic cells developed from prokaryotic ones with the essential change being the development of membrane-bounded organelles within the cytoplasm of the cell.

CHECK THE NET
You'll find some organelle labelling exercises at wsuonline.weber.edu/course.botany.130/unit1_la.htm

Complete the table to show differences between prokaryotic and eukaryotic cells.

PROKARYOTE AND EUKARYOTE CELLS

The table compares prokaryote and eukaryote cells:

Feature	Prokaryotic cells	Eukaryotic cells
nucleus	none	present
chromosomes	DNA in strands	present
membrane-bounded organelles	none	present e.g. mitochondria
mitosis or meiosis	none	one or both occur
ribosomes	smaller	larger

PROKARYOTIC CELLS

The diagram shows the structure of a prokaryotic cell e.g. bacterium.

Label parts A to H of the bacterial cell.

A	cell membrane	E	storage material
B	cell wall	F	ribosomes
C	flagella	G	plasmid
D	DNA	H	capsule

EUKARYOTIC CELLS

The diagram shows the structure of a generalized animal cell with details of organelles.

Label parts A to H of the cell.

A	mitochondrion	E	nucleolus
B	rough ER	F	secretory vesicle
C	Golgi apparatus	G	nucleus
D	nuclear pore	H	centriole

DON'T FORGET
Make sure you compare plant and animal cells.

EXAMINER'S SECRETS
You should be able to recognize the organelles in cells in electron micrographs.

Turn the page for some exam questions on this topic ▶

For more on this topic, see page 16 of the *Revision Express A-level Study Guide*

EXAM QUESTION 1

Attempt to compare the two types of cells.

(a) The table lists some of the features of cells. Complete the table by ticking in the appropriate column(s) if a feature is found in eukaryotes, prokaryotes or both.

Feature	Eukaryotes	Prokaryotes
usually less than 10 μm in size		✓
mitochondria present	✓	
enzymes present	✓	✓
ribosomes present	✓	✓
DNA often a continuous loop		✓
presence of a nuclear membrane	✓	

(b) Name one way in which the plant cell wall differs from that of most prokaryote cells.

Cellulose occurs only in the plant cell wall.

EXAM QUESTION 2

Tick the boxes to show which structures are present in the three groups of organisms.

WATCH OUT
Some structures are present in more than one group.

(a) The table compares animal, plant and bacterial cells. If the structure is a characteristic feature of the cell mark the appropriate box with a tick.

Structure	Animal	Plant	Bacterium
nuclear membrane	✓	✓	
circular DNA			✓
endoplasmic reticulum	✓	✓	
mitochondrion	✓	✓	
chloroplast		✓	
cell wall		✓	✓

(b) In the last 50 years major developments in biological techniques have revolutionized the study of cell organelles. Suggest a technique which has proved vital for the study of:

organelle structure	*electron microscopy*
organelle function	*differential centrifugation*

EXAM QUESTION 3

Have a go at interpreting the results of this experimental technique.

Chopped liver tissue was homogenized and the cell organelles present in the homogenate were then separated by centrifugation.

(a) Complete the table to show the order in which the mitochondria, nuclei and ribosomes would appear in the pellets at the bottom of the centrifuge tube after each centrifugation.

Speed (g)	Time (minutes)	Organelles in pellet
500–1000	10	*nuclei*
10 000–20 000	20	*mitochondria*
100 000	60	*ribosomes*

(b) What could be measured to show that the mitochondria obtained could still carry out their function?

Oxygen or ATP taken up.
Carbon dioxide or ATP produced.

SYLLABUS CHECK
Skip this question if you're doing the Edexcel, OCR or WJEC syllabuses.

© Pearson Education Limited 2001

Cell membrane

AQA/A AQA/B EDEXCEL OCR WJEC

The plasma membrane is the boundary which separates the living cell from its non-living surroundings. It exhibits the property of selective permeability, that is, it allows some substances to pass through it more easily than others.

STRUCTURE OF THE MEMBRANE

The principal biochemical constituents are phospholipid and protein. The diagram represents a phospholipid molecule.

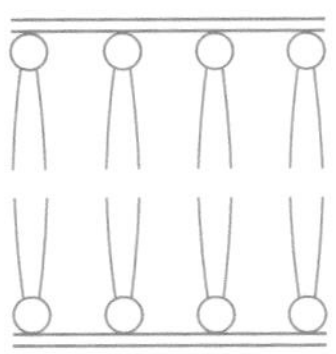

A	glycerol	hydrophilic (polar)
B	fatty acids	hydrophobic (non-polar)

> **Name the parts of the molecule** labelled A and B and state how they differ in their properties with respect to water.

> **THE JARGON**
> Hydrophilic means 'water-liking' or water soluble.

> **Use the simplified diagram** to show the arrangement of phospholipid molecules in a cell membrane. The sandwich model (1935) proposed that two protein layers can be added.
> Add the protein layers to your diagram.

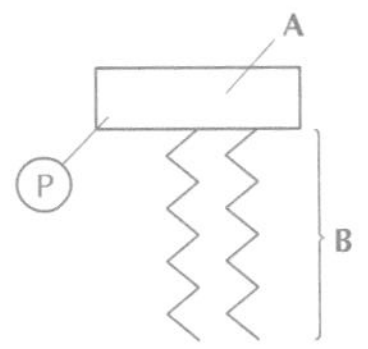

THE SELECTIVE PERMEABILITY OF THE MEMBRANE

Substances that move through the membrane do so at different rates. The graph shows the results of an investigation into the passage of various molecules across a cell membrane.

1. Urea has low oil solubility, so cannot move quickly.

2. Membrane has low permeability to urea.

3. Membrane has low permeability to glycerol ether.

4. Lipid soluble molecules are more permeable than water soluble molecules.

> **WATCH OUT**
> This is a difficult concept.
> The hydrophobic core of the membrane impedes the transport of ions and polar molecules. These require specific transport proteins to help them across.
> Very small molecules that are polar but uncharged e.g. water, can also pass through the membrane rapidly. Hydrophobic molecules such as oxygen and carbon dioxide which are soluble in lipid can cross the membrane with ease.

> **Some of the conclusions of the experiment are correct and some are incorrect. Place a T for true or F for false after each sentence.**

> **LINK**
> Water soluble molecules have to be moved across the membrane by other means. See page 35.

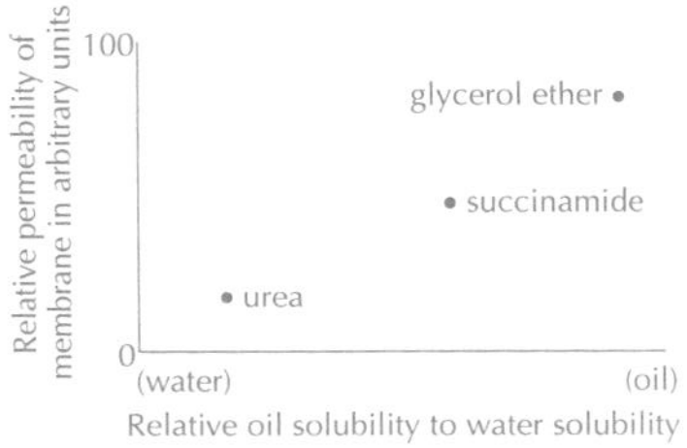

THE FLUID MOSAIC MODEL

Fluid	Most of the lipids and some of the proteins drift about randomly in the plane of the membrane.
Mosaic	A collage of many different proteins embedded in the fluid matrix of the lipid bilayer (the main fabric of the membrane).

> **Explain what is meant by the terms 'fluid' and 'mosaic' in this context.**

Turn the page for some exam questions on this topic ▶

EXAM QUESTION 1

The diagram shows the fluid mosaic structure of the cell membrane.

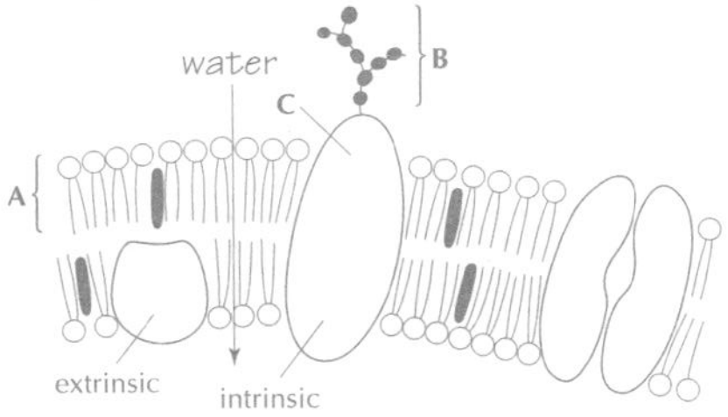

(a) **Complete the table by naming the parts of the membrane labelled A, B and C in the diagram and state the function of each.**

Structure	Name	Function
A	phospholipid	allows passage of liposoluble molecules
B	glycoprotein	cell recognition
C	protein	pump/receptor/active uptake/ facilitated transport

(b) **Draw an arrow on the diagram to show the path followed by water as it enters the cell.**

EXAM QUESTION 2

Give an account of the general structure of the cell membrane and describe briefly the functions of the membrane.

These factors may be mentioned in an ideal answer:

Main function is to serve as a boundary between cell and its environment. It is partially permeable. The main component is the bimolecular **phospholipid** layer with inwardly directed hydrophobic tails. It is capable of much movement i.e. is fluid. Other component – **protein** molecules with irregular arrangements:

- peripheral, found on the surface
- integral, extend into the phospholipid layer
- transmembrane, extend completely across.

Surface view shows that the proteins are dotted throughout the phospholipid layer in a **mosaic** arrangement.

Functions (with a descriptive sentence on each):

- structural support
- transport
- cell–cell recognition
- surface recognition by enzymes, hormones and antibodies.

> **Write out a plan for this essay question.**

> **EXAMINER'S SECRETS**
> Although called essay questions it is quite acceptable for you to include diagrams, even when these are not specifically requested. A well annotated diagram can often replace text, save time and can gain just as many marks. This question is a good example where you can do this.

Cell organelles

In addition to the plasma membrane at its outer surface, a eukaryotic cell has extensive and elaborately arranged internal membranes, which partition the cell into compartments. There are also non-membranous structures in the cell.

THE IMPORTANCE OF INTERNAL MEMBRANES

Internal membranes serve several important functions in cells:

- provide an internal transport system
- provide a large surface area for the attachment of enzymes and other reactants
- contain enzymes and/or potentially harmful reactants in membrane-bound organelles.

List three advantages of having membrane-bound organelles.

MEMBRANOUS ORGANELLES

Membranous organelles carry out a number of different functions.

Function of structure	Name
controls cell's activities and retains chromosomes	nucleus
site of respiration	mitochondrion
site of protein synthesis	(ribosome)/rough ER
site of photosynthesis	chloroplast
site of lipid and steroid synthesis	smooth ER
digests structures or molecules	lysosome

Complete the table by naming each structure.

SYLLABUS CHECK
Check your syllabus for the names of the organelles you need to study.

IF YOU HAVE TIME
This topic is ideal for preparing review notes in the form of a flow diagram, placing named organelles in boxes and linking them appropriately with their functions by means of arrows.

NON-MEMBRANOUS ORGANELLES

Non-membranous organelles also carry out a number of functions.

Function of structure	Name
synthesizes the spindle	centriole
transport, cytoskeleton, spindle in cell division, component of cilia	microtubules
assist in movement of material	cilia
increase surface area for absorption	microvilli

This time you complete the functions of these organelles.

DON'T FORGET
Make sure you study the cell wall. It is not an organelle but plays an important role in plant cells.

EXAMINER'S SECRETS
You need to study the various organelles in depth. The nucleus has been included to illustrate this point.

THE NUCLEUS

The statements describe parts of the nucleus.

the outer portion forms part of the endoplasmic reticulum	nuclear membrane
coils of DNA bound to proteins in the non-dividing cell	chromatin
its function is the assembly of the structural components of ribosomes	nucleolus
they make it possible for mRNA to reach the ribosomes.	nuclear pores

Identify the parts of the nucleus described.

Turn the page for some exam questions on this topic ▶

For more on this topic, see pages 18–19 of the *Revision Express A-level Study Guide*

EXAM QUESTION 1

The diagram shows part of a mitochondrion.

Label the parts of the diagram, then answer the questions.

(a) Label:

A ...... matrix
B ...... intermembranal space
C ...... crista

(b) Name the most abundant molecule found in structure D.

phospholipid

(c) (i) Explain why some cells have exceptionally large numbers of mitochondria.

energy requiring/very active/high metabolism

(ii) Give an example of a tissue which might contain such cells.

muscle/nerve/liver/secretory

EXAM QUESTION 2

The diagram shows the structure of the chloroplast as seen with an electron microscope.

Label the features A to E on the diagram of the organelle.

A ...... starch grain
B ...... double membrane
C ...... granum
D ...... thylakoid/intergranal lamella
E ...... stroma

EXAM QUESTION 3

The statements describe three membranous organelles.

Tick the boxes to answer this question.

EXAMINER'S SECRETS
You will need to tick more than one box in some horizontal rows.

	Rough endoplasmic reticulum	Smooth endoplasmic reticulum	Golgi body
continuous with outer nuclear membrane	✓	✓	
contains abundant ribosomes	✓		
site of lipid synthesis		✓	
main site of peptide bond formation	✓		
produces lysosomes			✓

Mitosis

Mitosis is the type of cell division which involves the distribution of identical genetic material, DNA, to two daughter cells. The DNA is copied exactly, so that, in humans each new cell receives 46 chromosomes.

CHROMOSOME STRUCTURE

Each chromosome consists of two threads called chromatids, joined at a point called the centromere. Chromosomes exist in homologous pairs:

A   chromatid   chromosomes have replicated
B   centromere

Chromosomes consist of a material called ..C... When chromosomes replicate they form identical sister ..D... These separate during mitosis, becoming the ...E... of the new daughter cells.

C chromatin   D chromatids   E chromosomes

Label A and B in diagram X.
Explain what has happened to the chromosomes in diagram Y.

THE JARGON
A homologous pair of chromosomes are the same length, have the centromere in the same position and carry the same genes (though not necessarily the same alleles of these genes) in identical positions.

CHECK THE NET
You'll find a mitosis tutorial at:
www.biology.arizona.edu/cell_bio/
tutorials/cell_cycle/main.html

Fill in the blanks C, D and E.

SIGNIFICANCE OF MITOSIS

- growth
- cell replacement/regeneration
- asexual reproduction.

List three ways in which an increase in cell number is important in living organisms.

STAGES IN MITOSIS

Dividing cells undergo a regular pattern of events, known as the cell cycle. The following statements describe the **main** events taking place in **animal** cells.

chromosomes attached to equator of spindle	metaphase
a period of intense chemical activity which includes the replication of DNA	interphase
chromatids pulled to opposite poles	anaphase
cytokinesis occurs	telophase
chromosomes shorten and thicken and spindle forms	prophase

Write the name of the appropriate stage in the boxes. Be careful, they're not in the correct order.

DON'T FORGET
The cell cycle lasts 8–24 hours in humans and the nuclear division occupies about 10% of this time.

Turn the page for some exam questions on this topic ▶

For more on this topic, see pages 20–21 of the *Revision Express A-level Study Guide*

EXAM QUESTION 1

The diagram shows a three-dimensional view of one of the stages of mitosis in a typical animal cell.

Name of the stage shown	metaphase
Name of structure labelled A	centromere
Function of structure labelled B	pulls chromatids to opposite poles

This question is easy. Don't be put off by the diagram because you have not seen the stage in this view before.

DON'T FORGET
The differences between mitosis cell division in plants and animals.

EXAM QUESTION 2

(a) Name a period in mitosis during which DNA replication takes place.

interphase

(b) The diagram shows the changes in the DNA content of a cell during one cell cycle.

(i) Which part of the diagram, I, II, III or IV, shows when DNA replication is taking place? Explain your answer.

II DNA content at the end of the phase is double that at the beginning

(ii) During which part of the diagram would you expect the chromosomes to have become visible?

III (18–24 hours)

(iii) Describe fully what is happening to the cell during the part of the diagram labelled IV.

- DNA content of the cell is halved.
- Daughter cells are produced, each containing the same amount of DNA that they had at the start.
- Cell divides by constriction/cell plate formation.
- Chromosomes become long and thin.
- Spindle fibres disappear; nuclear envelope reforms, nucleoli reappear.

(iv) What is the name given to this stage in mitosis?

telophase/cytokinesis

This question requires you to apply your knowledge of mitosis.

EXAMINER'S SECRETS
You would be expected to provide any three of these five answers.

Meiosis

Meiosis separates chromosomes, halving the diploid number, and introduces variation to the haploid products. It occurs in gamete formation.

SIGNIFICANCE OF MEIOSIS

Here are some key terms.

Term	Definition
gamete	sex cells produced by meiosis; sperm in male, ovum in female
diploid cell	with the full set of chromosomes in the nucleus
haploid cell	containing a single set of chromosomes
fertilization	the fusion of male and female gametes to form a zygote

Write out the definitions to the terms.

SYLLABUS CHECK
OCR, AQA(A), AQA(B) require the principles of meiosis only. Details of the stages of meiosis are *not* required.

IF YOU HAVE TIME
Make cards showing diagrams of the stages of meiosis. Practise putting the cards in the correct order and naming the stages correctly. (Hint: put the names of the stages on the back of the cards.)

In each generation, the doubling of chromosome number that results from fertilization, is offset by the halving of chromosome number that results from meiosis:

male parent (2n) → A → male gamete (n) → zygote (2n) → B → new individual
female parent (2n) → A → female gamete (n) → zygote (2n)

A meiosis
B mitosis

What type of cell division takes place at points A and B?

The list shows the diploid number of some plants and animals.

Human	46	23
Fruit fly	8	4
Onion	16	8
Potato	48	24

Give the number of chromosomes found in the gametes.

MEIOSIS AND GENETIC VARIETY

List three ways in which meiosis promotes genetic variety.
- Crossing over.
- Independent assortment.
- Random fertilization.

SYLLABUS CHECK
Skip this unless you are doing the WJEC syllabus.

Turn the page for some exam questions on this topic ▶

For more on this topic, see pages 142–143 of the *Revision Express A-level Study Guide*

EXAM QUESTION 1

The diagram shows four homologous pairs of chromosomes from a cell of the testis of the fruit fly, *Drosophila*.

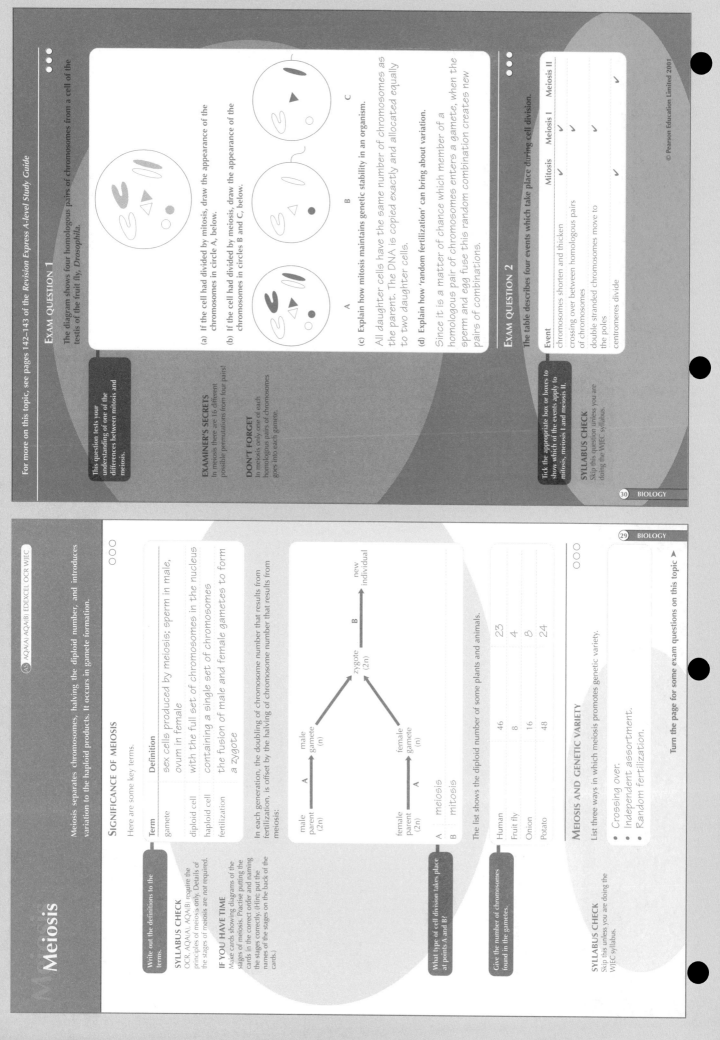

(a) If the cell had divided by mitosis, draw the appearance of the chromosomes in circle A, below.

(b) If the cell had divided by meiosis, draw the appearance of the chromosomes in circles B and C, below.

A   B   C

(c) Explain how mitosis maintains genetic stability in an organism.

All daughter cells have the same number of chromosomes as the parent. The DNA is copied exactly and allocated equally to two daughter cells.

(d) Explain how 'random fertilization' can bring about variation.

Since it is a matter of chance which member of a homologous pair of chromosomes enters a gamete, when the sperm and egg fuse this random combination creates new pairs of combinations.

This question tests your understanding of one of the differences between mitosis and meiosis.

EXAMINER'S SECRETS
In meiosis there are 16 different possible permutations from four pairs!

DON'T FORGET
In meiosis only one of each homologous pairs of chromosomes goes into each gamete.

EXAM QUESTION 2

The table describes four events which take place during cell division.

Event	Mitosis	Meiosis I	Meiosis II
chromosomes shorten and thicken	✓	✓	✓
crossing over between homologous pairs of chromosomes		✓	
double stranded chromosomes move to the poles	✓	✓	
centromeres divide	✓		✓

Tick the appropriate box or boxes to show which of the events apply to mitosis, meiosis I and meiosis II.

SYLLABUS CHECK
Skip this question unless you are doing the WJEC syllabus.

© Pearson Education Limited 2001

Gene technology 1

AS AQA(A) AQA(B) OCR WJEC

DNA technology has launched a revolution in biotechnology. It has enabled scientists to modify specific genes and move them between organisms as diverse as plants, animals and bacteria.

SYLLABUS CHECK
If you are studying the OCR syllabus very little detail is required.

Draw arrows to link the terms with the correct definitions.

RECOMBINANT DNA TECHNOLOGY

Here are some key terms and definitions.

1 Recombinant DNA	Enzymes used to synthesize DNA from mRNA in specific cells.	⑤
2 Plasmids	Enzymes which cut DNA molecules between specific base sequences.	③
3 Restriction enzymes	DNA which results from the combination of fragments from two different organisms.	①
4 DNA ligases	Circular loops of DNA found in bacteria.	②
5 Reverse transcriptases	Enzymes which join together portions of DNA.	④

WATCH OUT
You must understand the sequence of this process.

The diagram shows the use of enzymes to make recombinant DNA:

GAATTC
CTTAAG

DNA cut by enzyme X

AATTC / G — sticky end

DNA fragment produced by same enzyme as X

GAATTC
CTTAAG

sticky end — G / CTTAA

addition of a DNA fragment from another source

a possible combination: GAAAAC / CTTAAG

fragments sealed by enzyme Y

Enzyme X — restriction enzyme
Enzyme Y — DNA ligase

Name the enzymes X and Y involved in the sequence.

LINK
For more information see Mitosis on page 27.

A human gene may be cloned in a bacterial plasmid.

1. Isolate plasmid vector DNA and human DNA.
2. Grow bacteria in culture.
3. Add DNA ligase – to bond covalently.
4. Mix the DNA – they join by base pairing.
5. Cut both DNA isolates with same restriction enzyme.
6. Add recombinant plasmid into bacterium (cloning vector).
7. Tag bacteria using antibiotic resistant sequence.
8. Insert human DNA into plasmids.

The main steps in cloning a human gene are in the wrong order. Place them in the correct order, starting with step 1.

1-5-8-4-3-6-7-2

Turn the page for some exam questions on this topic ▶

31 BIOLOGY

For more on this topic, see pages 22–23 of the *Revision Express A-level Study Guide*

EXAM QUESTION 1

Biologists in Australia plan to use genetic engineering to produce a gene which they intend to insert into orange trees. They have combined two pieces of DNA to produce a gene which they have called SDLS-2. The parts of this gene are:

DNA sequence that switches on a gene used in seed formation | gene that kills cells

Try this question on genetically engineered oranges.

(a) Explain how biologists could use enzymes:
(i) to remove a gene from a longer piece of DNA.

Restriction endonucleases are used to cut the DNA between specific sequences.

(ii) to join the two pieces together to make the SDLS-2 gene.

Using ligase enzyme.

(b) Suggest how the SDLS-2 gene might affect the production of the fruit.

Kill the cells that are going to produce seeds.

(c) Describe the likely advantage of the gene and any possible dangers that might result from growing plants containing this gene.

Seedless oranges have greater economic value.
If the gene gets into another species it could result in sterility.

EXAM QUESTION 2

The diagram represents part of the process in the production of a crop plant resistant to the broad-spectrum weedkiller, glyphosate. A represents the gene for glyphosate resistance.

plasmid 1

engineered plasmid which is introduced into a crop plant

This question asks some of the same points but in a different way. It also takes the process of DNA recombination one step further.

EXAMINER'S SECRETS
Don't be put off by words like 'glyphosate'.
Examiners have to put questions like this into a true context. It should not affect your ability to answer the question.

(a) (i) Name the specific biological molecule X which makes up the plasmid.

DNA

(ii) Name the enzyme types represented by D and E.

D — *restriction endonuclease*
E — *ligase*

(iii) The diagram shows the sticky ends on A in detail. Enter the base sequence you would expect to find on sticky ends B and C of the plasmid.

B *TTA* C *CGA*

(b) Suggest one advantage to farmers of growing crops resistant to glyphosate.

Spraying with glyphosate will only kill the weeds.

32 BIOLOGY

Gene technology II

DNA technology is in the news almost every day! Usually the topic of the story is a new and promising application to a medical problem. However, DNA technology has also raised questions about possible dangerous consequences of its use.

GENE THERAPY

An example of successful gene therapy involves the treatment of cystic fibrosis.

SYLLABUS CHECK
Skip gene therapy if you're studying the AQA(B) syllabus.

Draw arrows to link the correct descriptions with the appropriate terms.

THE JARGON
In cystic fibrosis the transregulator protein (CFTR) is defective.

1 Gene therapy	The CFTR gene codes for a protein which is essential for chloride transport. A defective gene lacks the ability to produce just one particular amino acid.	③
2 Symptoms	DNA sample collected from blood cells. Copies made using DNA polymerase and run on an electrophoresis gel. The CFTR gene will have a three-base deletion and will move more quickly.	④
3 Cause	Wrapping the gene in lipid molecules that can pass through the membranes of the lung cells.	⑤
4 Diagnostic test	Thick, sticky mucus clogs up the lungs and blocks the pancreatic duct.	②
5 Treatment	The insertion of a new DNA sequence to counteract a faulty gene.	①

THE JARGON
Electrophoresis is a technique used to separate molecules at different electric charge. The speed with which a molecule moves towards an electrode is affected by the amount of the charge and the size of the molecule. Thus, small fragments, with the same charge, move faster than large ones.

GENETIC FINGERPRINTING

The following are the main stages involved in genetic fingerprinting.

Describe briefly the purpose of each step in the process.

restriction enzymes	to cut DNA into fragments
electrophoresis	to sort DNA fragments according to size
radioactive probes	to locate specific DNA fragments (core sequences)
X-ray film	the probes on the DNA expose the film, revealing a pattern of light and dark bands

THE JARGON
The light and dark bands make up the pattern known as the genetic fingerprint.

Genetic fingerprinting is used in two main areas:

Forensic science and paternity testing.

Give two uses of genetic fingerprinting.

DNA TECHNOLOGY RAISES IMPORTANT SAFETY, MORAL AND ETHICAL ISSUES

IF YOU HAVE TIME
Gather information from a variety of sources and read generally around the subject so that you obtain a balanced viewpoint of this important issue.

DNA technology is:
- reshaping medicine and the pharmaceutical industry
- providing forensic, environmental and agricultural applications
- raising important safety and ethical questions.

The advantages and disadvantages of DNA technology, together with the ethical issues raised will be considered in the exam question section overleaf.

Turn the page for some exam questions on this topic ➤

For more on this topic, see pages 150–151 of the *Revision Express A-level Study Guide*

EXAM QUESTION 1

In an investigation involving genetic fingerprinting, DNA was extracted from a blood sample and broken into fragments using a restriction enzyme. The diagram shows the resulting separation of these fragments by electrophoresis.

Interpret this electrophoresis pattern.

size of fragment (kilobase pairs)

20.7
6.95
5.92
5.53
4.70
3.29

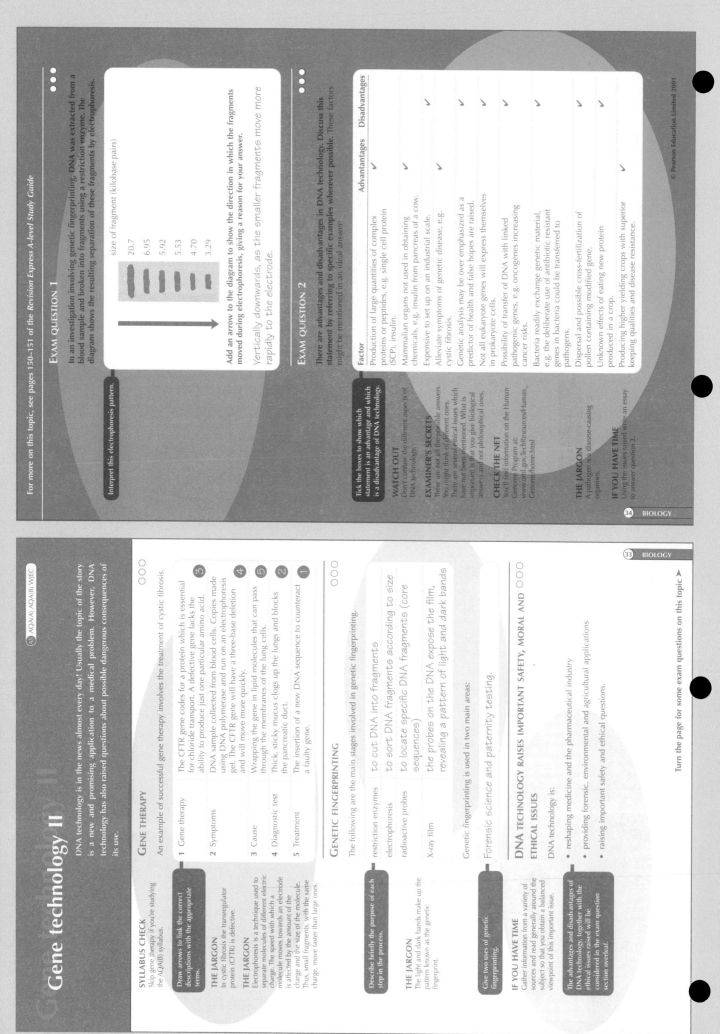

Add an arrow to the diagram to show the direction in which the fragments moved during electrophoresis, giving a reason for your answer.

Vertically downwards, as the smaller fragments move more rapidly to the electrode.

EXAM QUESTION 2

There are advantages and disadvantages in DNA technology. Discuss this statement by referring to specific examples wherever possible. These factors might be mentioned in an ideal answer.

Tick the boxes to show which statement is an advantage and which is a disadvantage of DNA technology.

WATCH OUT
Don't confuse the different aspects of DNA technology.

EXAMINER'S SECRETS
These are not all the possible answers. You might think of different ones. There are several ethical issues which have not been mentioned. What is important is that you give biological answers and not philosophical ones.

CHECK THE NET
You'll find information on the Human Genome Program at: www.ornl.gov/TechResources/Human_Genome/home.html

THE JARGON
A pathogen is a disease-causing organism.

IF YOU HAVE TIME
Using the issues raised write an essay to answer question 2.

Factor	Advantages	Disadvantages
Production of large quantities of complex proteins or peptides, e.g. single cell protein (SCP), insulin.	✓	
Mammalian organs not used in obtaining chemicals, e.g. insulin from pancreas of a cow.	✓	
Expensive to set up on an industrial scale.		✓
Alleviate symptoms of genetic disease, e.g. cystic fibrosis.	✓	
Genetic analysis may be over emphasized as a predictor of health and false hopes are raised.		✓
Not all eukaryote genes will express themselves in prokaryote cells.		✓
Possibility of transfer of DNA with linked pathogenic genes, e.g. oncogenes increasing cancer risks.		✓
Bacteria readily exchange genetic material, e.g. the deliberate use of antibiotic resistant genes in bacteria could be transferred to pathogens.		✓
Dispersal and possible cross-fertilization of pollen containing modified gene.		✓
Unknown effects of eating new protein produced in a crop.		✓
Producing higher yielding crops with superior keeping qualities and disease resistance.	✓	

© Pearson Education Limited 2001

Passive transport of molecules

(AS) AQA(A) AQA(B) EDEXCEL OCR WJEC

A steady traffic of small molecules moves across the plasma membrane in both directions. Molecules have kinetic energy within them called thermal motion. One result of this thermal motion is diffusion.

THE JARGON
Passive transport does not involve the use of energy

TRANSPORT PROCESSES

The processes of passive transport of molecules across a biological membrane include diffusion, osmosis and facilitated diffusion. Here are definitions of these processes.

Use the correct term for each of the definitions.

The process by which a substance moves from where it is more concentrated to where it is less concentrated.	diffusion
Diffusion with the help of carrier and channel proteins.	facilitated diffusion
The movement of water from a solution of less negative water potential to a solution of more negative water potential through a partially permeable membrane.	osmosis

EXAMINER'S SECRETS
A useful term is 'concentration gradient' whereby molecules move down a concentration gradient from high to low.

THE JARGON
Water potential (WP) is the capacity of water to leave a system. Pure water has a WP of zero. All solutions have a negative WP.

DIFFUSION

The rate of diffusion depends on several factors:

Place a tick alongside one of each pair of factors which will increase the rate of diffusion.

temperature	high	✓	low	
concentration gradient	small		large	✓
surface area	large	✓	small	
membrane	thin	✓	thick	
pores in membrane	many	✓	few	
solubility in water or lipid	water		lipid	✓
size of molecules	large		small	✓

DON'T FORGET
Make sure you are familiar with Fick's law.

DON'T FORGET
Polar molecules and ions are impeded by the lipid bilayer of the membrane.

SPEED LEARNING
Think of the o in hypo as being low in concentration.

OSMOSIS

Osmosis in biological systems usually occurs when a membrane separates two solutions of different concentrations. Some terms used are hypertonic, hypotonic and isotonic.

Water moves from a more dilute or ...A... solution to a more concentrated or ...B... solution. When both solutions are of equal concentrations they are said to be ...C....

Fill in the blanks A, B and C with the appropriate word.

A hypotonic   B hypertonic   C isotonic

THE JARGON
Turgid – the vacuole is full of water and the cytoplasm (protoplast) is pushed against the cell wall.

There are differences between plants and animal cells when placed in solutions.

Complete the table and in the space beneath explain the difference in terms of cell structure.

Concentration of solution	Effect on animal cell	Effect on plant cell
hypotonic	cell will burst	cell becomes turgid
hypertonic	cell will shrink	cell becomes flaccid

Plant cells have a cell wall.

SYLLABUS CHECK
Only the WJEC syllabus requires the use of a given equation to determine water potential.

Turn the page for some exam questions on this topic ▶

EXAM QUESTION 1

A respiring cell gains oxygen by the process of simple diffusion; it gains most of its glucose by facilitated diffusion.

(a) Give one similarity and one difference between the two processes.

Similarity	Difference
Movement from high to low concentration/no energy required.	A carrier or protein is needed in facilitated diffusion/it is specific – can transport selected molecules.

(b) The rate of diffusion through a membrane is proportional to:

$$\frac{\text{surface area} \times \text{difference in concentration}}{\text{thickness of membrane}}$$

Suggest whether the values of each of the three variables will be high or low when the rate of diffusion through the membrane is at a minimum.

surface area — high
difference in concentration — high
thickness of membrane — low

Try this question which is about diffusion.

IF YOU HAVE TIME
There are a lot of terms and definitions to learn. Make a list of them all on cards or on a chart.

DON'T FORGET
This is Fick's law.

CHECK THE NET
You'll find information on the cellular movement of water at: carroll1.cc.edu/~jrlausz/botany/Water Movement.html

EXAM QUESTION 2

An artificial cell consisting of an aqueous solution enclosed in a selectively permeable membrane has just been immersed in a beaker containing a different solution. The membrane is permeable to water and to the simple sugars glucose and fructose, but completely impermeable to the disaccharide sucrose.

cell
0.2 M glucose
0.4 M sucrose

beaker solution
0.1 M sucrose
0.1 M glucose
0.1 M fructose

A

B

(a) Which solute will show a net diffusion into the cell? — fructose
(b) Which solute will show a net diffusion out of the cell? — glucose
(c) Which solution, A or B, is hypertonic? — A
(d) In which direction will there be a net osmotic movement of water? — into cell
(e) After the cell is placed in the beaker, will it become flaccid or turgid? — turgid

This question tests your understanding of osmosis and diffusion.

Other methods of molecular transport

(AS) AQA(A) AQA(B) EDEXCEL OCR WJEC

There are occasions when molecules need to be transported across the membrane against a concentration gradient, e.g. mineral ion transport. In addition, large molecules such as proteins and polysaccharides generally cross the membrane by entirely different mechanisms involving vesicles.

ACTIVE TRANSPORT ○○○

Active transport takes place via the carrier proteins that span the membrane.

1. There is a low concentration of glucose molecules outside the cell.
2. ATP attaches to the membrane protein on the inside of the cell.
3. The protein changes shape (active configuration) and glucose molecules are open to the inside of the membrane and closed to the outside.
4. Glucose molecules are taken up from outside the membrane by being bound to a carrier protein.
5. The carrier protein reverts to its binding configuration.
6. Glucose molecules are released with the aid of energy from ATP.

1-4-2-3-6-5

> **Put the points explaining how a carrier protein operates in active transport in the correct order.**

THE JARGON
ATP is often described as the energy currency of the cell. When molecules of ATP are hydrolysed, energy is released for reactions where it is needed in cells.

LINK
For more information on the structure of membranes, see page 23.

Any factor which affects the rate of respiration affects the rate of active transport.

Factor	Increase rate	Decrease rate
large number of mitochondria	✓	
high concentration of ATP	✓	
low temperature		✓
high oxygen level	✓	
low concentration of cyanide		✓

> **Tick the boxes to show whether the rate of active uptake is affected by the factors.**

EXAMINER'S SECRETS
You could be asked to explain some or all of these responses in an exam question.
Hints: temperature affects enzymes; cyanide is a respiratory poison.

TRANSPORT OF LARGE MOLECULES ○○○

Here are some sentences describing how large molecules enter and leave a cell.

A transport vesicle budded from the Golgi apparatus is moved to the plasma membrane. When they come in contact the two membranes fuse and the contents of the vesicle spills to the outside of the cell.

exocytosis

A small area of the plasma membrane sinks inwards to form a pocket. As the pocket develops, it pinches in, forming a vesicle containing material that had been outside the cell.

endocytosis

A cell engulfs a particle and packages it within a membrane-enclosed sac or vacuole.

phagocytosis

A cell engulfs droplets of extracellular fluid in tiny vesicles.

pinocytosis

> **Give the term that describes each process.**

SPEED LEARNING
Exo-exit-out.

LINK
For more information on cell organelles, see page 25.

Turn the page for some exam questions on this topic ➤

For more on this topic, see page 29 of the *Revision Express A-level Study Guide*

EXAM QUESTION 1

Measurements were made on the rate of uptake of two different substances, A and B, across the plasma membrane of cells. In each experiment, cells were placed in a known concentration of either A or B and the results of all the experiments are plotted in the graph. At the start of each experiment the internal concentration of A and B within the cells was 50 mM l^{-1} in each case.

> This exam question requires you to interpret the graph. It gets harder as it goes along!

(a) From the graph state the condition that is essential for the transport of A to take place.

The external concentration must be greater than the internal concentration.

(b) What process is responsible for the type of transport shown by A?

diffusion

(c) (i) What name is given to the type of transport shown by B?

active transport

   (ii) Give one piece of evidence to support your answer.

Uptake occurs against a concentration gradient when external conc. is greater than internal.

   (iii) Apart from B, name two other molecules associated with the membrane, which are needed for this process to occur.

protein and ATP

(d) (i) Compare the rate of uptake of B between 25 and 50 mM l^{-1} (external concentration) with the increase between 125 and 150 mM l^{-1}.

The rate of uptake doubles between 25 and 50 mM l^{-1} but there is virtually no increase between 125 and 150 mM l^{-1}.

   (ii) Explain the reason for this difference.

At low external concentrations there is a surplus of available protein carriers in the membrane but at high external concentrations the availability of carriers becomes rate-limiting.

Or 'protein carriers are saturated'.

IF YOU HAVE TIME
Try this essay question.
'Describe the various ways in which materials in solution can cross the membrane boundary of a cell. In each case discuss the factors which govern transmission.'

WATCH OUT
Be careful to refer to the rate of uptake and not just uptake.

Human digestion

AS AQA(B) EDEXCEL WJEC

Digestion is the process of breaking down food into molecules small enough for the body to absorb across the intestinal lining into the blood. Some nutrients are transported across the lining by passive means while the absorption of other nutrients is by active transport.

SYLLABUS CHECK
The Edexcel syllabus requires you to study carbohydrate digestion only.

THE HUMAN DIGESTIVE SYSTEM

This is a simplified diagram of the human gut:

Name the parts labelled A to H.

A oesophagus   E gall bladder
B stomach   F bile duct
C duodenum   G large intestine
D ileum   H pancreas

The three main food types are broken down to their basic components by specific enzymes.

Complete the table by giving the names of the enzymes.

Food type	Enzymes	Action of enzyme
carbohydrate	amylase	starch to maltose
	maltase	maltose to glucose
protein	peptidase: endo-peptidase	hydrolyse peptide bonds between amino acids in the central region of proteins
	exo-peptidase	hydrolyse peptide bonds on the terminal amino acids of the portions, progressively reducing them to individual amino acids
fat	lipase	lipids to fatty acids and glycerol

LINK
For more information on enzymes see page 15.

SYLLABUS CHECK
The Edexcel syllabus requires you to study the histology of the ileum wall. The AQA(B) syllabus requires you to know about the generalized structure of the human gut wall as well as features of the different regions.

ABSORPTION

Efficient absorption is dependent in part on a large surface area being available.

List four adaptations of the wall of the ileum for efficient absorption.

- It is long.
- Its walls are folded.
- The folds have numerous villi.
- The epithelial cells lining the villi are covered with microvilli, forming a brush border.

LINK
For more information on molecular transport mechanisms see pages 35 and 37.

Turn the page for some exam questions on this topic ▶

For more on this topic, see pages 30–31 of the *Revision Express A-level Study Guide*

EXAM QUESTION 1

Try this recall question. Complete the table, which summarizes the digestion of selected substrates.

Enzyme	Site of secretion	Substrate	Products
endopeptidase/ pepsin	stomach	protein	polypeptides/peptides
exopeptidase	pancreas	peptides	amino acids
amylase	intestinal gland	starch	maltose

EXAM QUESTION 2

This question concentrates on fat digestion and absorption.

(a) Name the region of the digestive system where most fat digestion occurs.
duodenum

(b) Name the enzyme which is responsible for the digestion of fat.
lipase

(c) Name the site of secretion of this enzyme.
pancreas

(d) Describe fully the part played by liver in the digestion of fat.
The liver produces bile which reduces the surface tension of fat globules, emulsifying them so that a larger surface area is exposed to enzyme activity.
Bile also raises the pH to the optimum for lipase.

(e) Describe how digested lipids may be absorbed from the gut.
Fatty acids and glycerol diffuse through the epithelial membrane of the gut wall, then recombine. Small droplets pass into the lacteals of the lymphatic system by pinocytosis.

EXAM QUESTION 3

The electron micrograph diagram shows some of the cells forming part of the epithelial lining of the human small intestine.

SYLLABUS CHECK
Study the diagram carefully before answering the question.

SYLLABUS CHECK
Check that your syllabus requires you to be able to interpret electron micrograph diagrams in this topic.

(a) Name the features labelled A and B and explain how they function in this tissue.

A microvilli   increase surface area for absorption
B mitochondria   provide energy for active transport

(b) Name the secretion labelled C.
mucus/mucin

Transport and exchange mechanisms

AS AQA(B) EDEXCEL WJEC

Living things need to obtain materials such as carbon dioxide and oxygen from the environment and remove waste from their cells to the environment. Efficient exchange mechanisms require the surface area over which transfer is to occur to be large compared with the volume of the organism.

SIZE AND SURFACE AREA

With increase in size the surface area to volume ratio is decreased and exchange demand by simple diffusion is inadequate. An increase in metabolic rate also makes diffusion insufficient to supply demand. The table shows various dimensions of animal tissue.

Length of side (cm)	Volume (cm³)	Ratio of surface area:volume
1	1	6:1
2	8	3:1
3	27	2:1

Doubling the length halves the ratio/the size of the ratio is inversely proportional to the length.

Organism	Surface area: volume ratio	Modification	Exchange surface
unicellular protozoan	large	small	membrane
flatworm	large	flat	surface
earthworm	small	slow moving	moist skin
fish	small	specialized exchange surface	gill
mammal	small	specialized exchange surface	lung

SPEED LEARNING
If you find the concept of surface area to volume ratio difficult consider it this way. *If the overall shape is kept the same, an increase in size means an increased distance from the surface to the centre of the organism.*

Using the information in the table, state in words, the **quantitative** relationship between length and surface area:volume ratio.

Complete the table that summarizes how different animals have overcome the problem of obtaining materials from the environment.

LINK
For more information on diffusion, see page 35.

THE EXCHANGE SURFACE

The requirements of an efficient exchange surface:

*   large surface area
*   permeable
*   thin
*   moist.

In addition animals which have evolved specialized exchange surfaces need:

*   an efficient transport system
*   a ventilation mechanism
*   an intimate contact between the transport system and the medium to be exchanged.

List the requirements of an efficient respiratory exchange surface.

LINK
Specialized exchange surfaces are dealt with in more detail on page 43.

List the additional requirements of fish and mammals.

Turn the page for some exam questions on this topic ➤

For more on this topic, see page 32 of the *Revision Express A-level Study Guide*

EXAM QUESTION 1

Diagram A illustrates the size and shape of *Amoeba* (a single celled organism) and diagram B illustrates *Planaria* (a flatworm).

Have a go at answering a question about diffusion in small organisms.

0.1 mm ⟷ A

15.0 mm ⟷ B

(a) For each animal, explain why simple diffusion provides an adequate gaseous exchange between the organism and its environment.

Amoeba   It is small and has a large surface area to volume ratio, so gases do not have far to diffuse/short diffusion path.

Planaria   Although relatively large, it is flat and so has a large surface area to volume ratio and each cell is a short distance from the surface/short diffusion path.

(b) Explain why both animals can only exist in water.

On land water would be lost through their surface and they would suffer dessication.

EXAM QUESTION 2

This question requires you to consider adaptations needed to overcome an increase in size.

(a) Explain why an increase in size in animals makes respiratory exchange more difficult.

The uptake of oxygen is proportional to the area of the absorbing surface/the uptake of oxygen is proportional to the volume of the tissue. An increase in size means that the surface area:volume ratio is reduced and oxygen must diffuse over a greater distance, making the process inadequate.

(b) Suggest three different ways in which animals overcome this problem.

*   The possession of a flat or thin shape.
*   The development of special, large gas exchange surfaces e.g. gills, lungs.
*   Having a lower metabolic rate/becoming less active.
*   The development of circulatory systems/reference to a respiratory pigment.
*   The development of ventilating systems.

Gas exchange in bony fish

Fish obtain oxygen from water by means of gills.

GILL STRUCTURE

The diagram shows the operculum (gill cover) removed to show the gills.

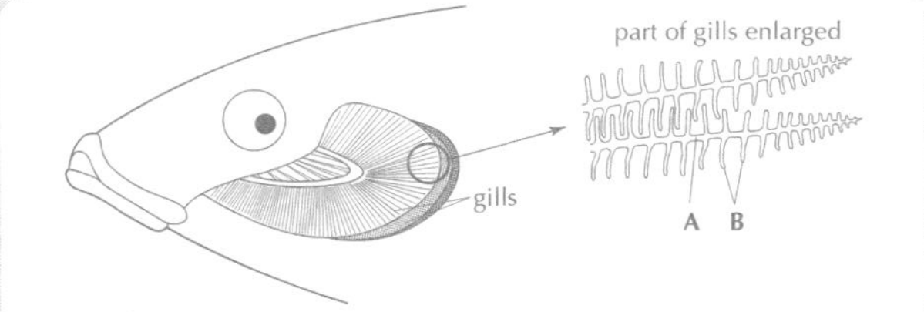

part of gills enlarged

gills

A

B

Label parts A and B.

A   gill filament

B   gill lamellae

The gills also have an extensive network of blood capillaries to allow efficient diffusion, and haemoglobin for the carriage of oxygen.

VENTILATION MECHANISM

Water is a dense medium with a low oxygen content, so it needs to be forced over the gill filaments by pressure differences. This maintains a continuous, unidirectional flow of water.

Complete the table by inserting the appropriate word.

	Water intake	Water expulsion
mouth	opens	closed
operculum	closed	open
floor of buccal cavity	lowered	raised
volume	increases	decreases
pressure	decreases	increases

DON'T FORGET

A lower pressure is maintained in the opercular cavity than in the bucco-pharynx.
The operculum acts as both a valve permitting water out and as a pump drawing water past the gill filaments. The mouth also acts as a pump and together with the actions of the operculum, delivers an almost continuous flow of water over the gills.

COUNTER CURRENT FLOW

Efficient gaseous exchange is achieved by the stream of water flowing over the gills and the blood flow through the gills being in opposite directions:

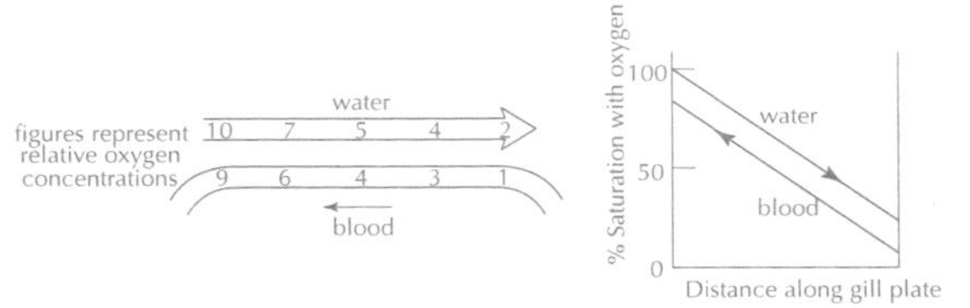

figures represent relative oxygen concentrations

water
10 7 5 4 2

blood
9 6 4 3 1

% Saturation with oxygen

100

50

0

gill plate

water

blood

Distance along gill plate

Explain how the counter current flow increases the efficiency of gaseous exchange.

The blood always meets water with a relatively higher oxygen content, maintaining a concentration gradient throughout the whole length of the gill filament.

Turn the page for some exam questions on this topic ▶

EXAM QUESTION 1

The diagram shows a structure adapted for gaseous exchange.

You should find this first question quite easy.

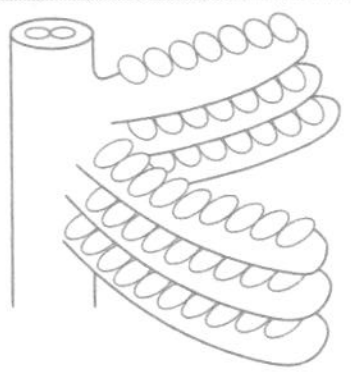

(a) Name the group of animals in which the structure is found.

fish

(b) State two features of the structure which aid efficient gaseous exchange.

- Large surface area of gills.
- Thin and permeable gill plates.

(c) State how a continuous supply of oxygen reaches the surface of the structure.

Water enters through the mouth, over the gills and out through the operculum.

(d) Explain why the structure could not function in a land animal.

The gills would lack support out of water and would collapse, reducing their surface area.

EXAMINER'S SECRETS

Since the question asks you to state rather than explain there is no need to go into the details of the ventilation mechanism here.

EXAM QUESTION 2

The diagram shows a gill plate of a bony fish.

This question covers the same topic but goes into more detail.

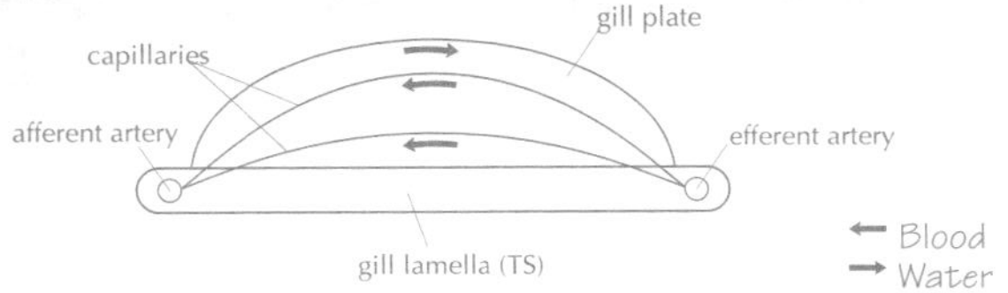

efferent artery

gill plate

capillaries

afferent artery

gill lamella (TS)

↓ Blood
↑ Water

(a) (i) Draw arrows on the capillaries to indicate the direction of the blood flow.

(ii) Draw and label an arrow to indicate the flow of water over the gill plate.

(b) Describe three ways, other than the flow arrangement, in which the gill filament is adapted as a respiratory surface.

- It is sub-divided to increase the surface for gas exchange.
- The tips of adjacent gill filaments overlap, increasing resistance to water flow, slowing the passage of water over the gill lamellae, thus increasing the time available for gas exchange.
- There is a good blood supply.
- A diffusion gradient is maintained.

Gas exchange in plants

AS AQA(B) EDEXCEL WJEC

To make food a plant must provide a large surface area, the leaves, to the sun and obtain carbon dioxide from the air. CO_2 diffuses into the leaf, and O_2, produced as a by-product of photosynthesis, diffuses out of the leaf through the stomata.

LEAF STRUCTURE

The diagram is a transverse section of a leaf.

A   cuticle   F   air space
B   upper epidermis   G   guard cell
C   palisade mesophyll H   stoma
D   spongy mesophyll   I   chloroplasts
E   lower epidermis

The leaf is well adapted for gaseous exchange.

- The leaf is thin, providing a short diffusion path, and has a large surface area.
- The spongy mesophyll is permeated by air spaces.
- The epidermis has numerous stomata.

MECHANISM OF OPENING AND CLOSING OF STOMATA

Guard cells, by controlling the opening and closing of stomata, help balance the plant's need to conserve water with its requirement for photosynthesis.

1. In the light, guard cells increase their turgor by actively transporting potassium ions (K⁺) from adjacent cells to the guard cells.
2. K⁺ ions lower the water potential and cause water to move in by osmosis.
3. The pairs of cells curve away from each other and the pore opens.
4. The pumping of K⁺ ions requires energy.
5. Guard cells become turgid and swell.
6. Guard cells do not expand uniformly as the inner wall is thicker and less elastic than the outer wall.
7. Energy is provided from photosynthesis and this is why guard cells contain chloroplasts.

1-4-7-2-5-6-3

Turn the page for some exam questions on this topic ▶

WATCH OUT
The direction of diffusion depends on environmental conditions and the requirements of the plant.
During the day the overall gas released is O_2, because the rate of photosynthesis is greater than the rate of respiration. At night only respiration occurs, so the gas released is CO_2.

Label the parts A to I.

Using a coloured pen trace the pathway of CO_2 diffusion through the leaf.

List three ways in which the leaf is adapted for efficient gas exchange.

Starting with statement 1 place the stages of the *opening mechanism* of stomata in the correct order.

DON'T FORGET
Guard cells control the diameter of the stoma by changing shape, thereby narrowing or widening the gap between the two cells. They are the only cells in the epidermal layer to contain chloroplasts.

SYLLABUS CHECK
Skip the mechanism if you're studying the AQA(B) syllabus.

For more on this topic, see pages 32–33 of the *Revision Express A-level Study Guide*

EXAM QUESTION 1

Give an illustrated account of the structure of the leaf (excluding vascular tissue) as seen in a high power section. Describe how the structure of the leaf is related to its function.

These factors might be mentioned in an ideal answer.

waterproofing layer	cuticle
layer of protection	upper epidermis
site of photosynthesis	palisade layer
site of gaseous diffusion	spongy meosophyll
allow passage of gases between cells and outside via stomata	intercellular air spaces
diffusion of O_2, CO_2, and water vapour in and out of leaf	stoma
aid in opening and closing mechanism	guard cells
large surface area, thin for gas exchange and trapping of light	leaf lamina
contain pigments to trap light	chloroplasts

EXAMINER'S SECRETS
You will lose marks if you do not provide a diagram (and of good quality).

Fill in the boxes with the appropriate leaf structure

IF YOU HAVE TIME
Use the table to write out a *full* answer to the question. Include a diagram similar to that on the previous page.

EXAM QUESTION 2

Stomata are found on the underside of leaves. The diagram shows a stoma in surface view.

(a) **Label parts A to D.**

A guard cell   C stoma or pore
B thick inner wall   D chloroplasts

(b) **Explain why stomata are usually confined to the lower surface of leaves.**
Heat energy from sunlight enhances evaporation.
Water loss is reduced by having stomata on the lower (shaded) surface.

(c) **Explain how the opening and closing mechanism of stomata is related to the *structure of the guard cells.***

- Chloroplasts provide energy in the form of ATP for the pumping of K⁺ ions.
- The inner wall is thicker and inflexible. When the cell becomes turgid the guard cells do not expand uniformly and the pair of cells move away from each other and the pore opens.

This question concentrates on the stomata.

EXAM QUESTION 1

The diagram shows part of the wall of an alveolus and a section across a blood capillary.

> This question is about gas exchange in the lungs.

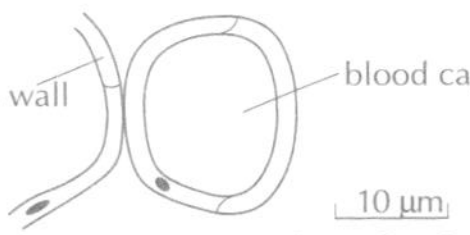

alveolus wall

blood capillary

10 μm

(a) Name the process by which oxygen passes from the alveolus to the capillary.

diffusion

(b) The width of the wall of the alveolus and the flow of blood in the capillary both affect the efficiency of the process.
Explain how each affects the process.

| width of the wall | Thin, flattened cells make the diffusion distance short. |
| flow of blood | O_2 is transported away by the blood, maintaining a steep diffusion gradient. |

(c) As the carbon dioxide concentration in the alveoli increases, the amount of air taken in by respiratory movements also increases. State two ways in which the respiratory movements change to achieve this effect.

- Increasing the depth of inspirations.
- Increasing the frequency of inspirations.

EXAM QUESTION 2

Each of the graphs shows a trace obtained on a spirometer's recording apparatus. Each peak shows the volume of air breathed in and each trough shows the volume breathed out. The small fluctuations show breathing in a resting person, the large fluctuations show the maximum inhalation and expiration the person could achieve. Trace A was obtained from a healthy person and trace B from a typical asthma sufferer.

> Look back at the definitions on the previous page before attempting this question.

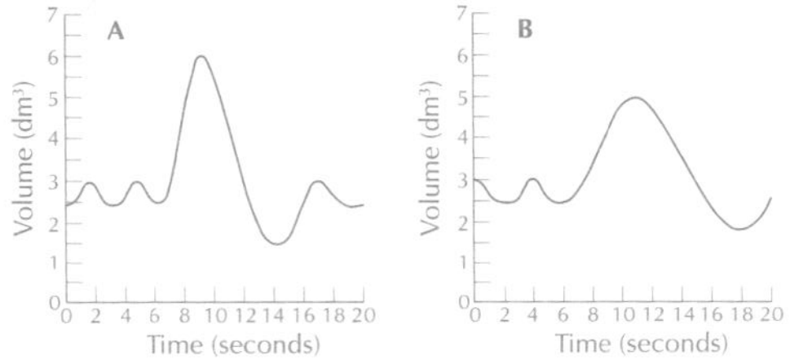

A

Volume (dm³)

0 2 4 6 8 10 12 14 16 18 20
Time (seconds)

B

Volume (dm³)

0 2 4 6 8 10 12 14 16 18 20
Time (seconds)

(a) For the healthy subject give:

the tidal volume   0.5 dm³   the vital capacity   4.5 dm³

(b) Compare the normal trace and the trace for the asthma sufferer. Give two ways in which the traces differ and one way in which they are the same.

| Differences | Vital capacity is less in asthmatic/peak is lower. Longer time taken to expire. |
| Similarity | Tidal volume is the same. |

(AS) AQA(A) AQA(B) EDEXCEL OCR WJEC

Gas exchange in mammals

Mammals are active and have evolved internal lungs which are adapted for exchange with air, a less dense medium than water.

STRUCTURE OF RESPIRATORY SYSTEM

The diagram shows the human respiratory system.

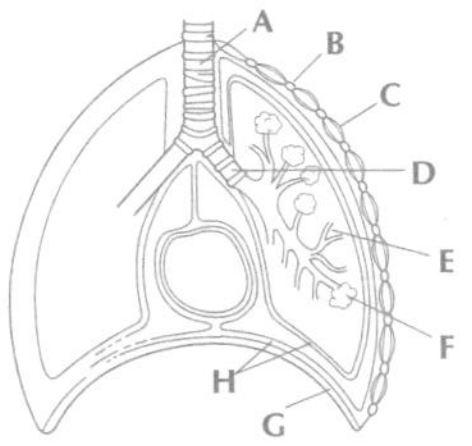

A B C D E F G H

A	trachea	E	bronchiole
B	rib	F	alveoli
C	intercostal muscle	G	diaphragm
D	bronchus	H	pleural membranes

> Label the parts A to H.

DON'T FORGET
Lungs supply a large surface area, increased by alveoli, lined with moisture for the dissolving of gases, thin walls to shorten diffusion path and an extensive capillary network for rapid diffusion and transport, to maintain diffusion gradients.

VENTILATION OF THE LUNGS

Mammals ventilate their lungs by negative pressure breathing, forcing air down into the lungs.

	Inspiration	Expiration
external intercostal muscle	contracts	relaxes
ribs	up and out	down and in
diaphragm	contracts and flattens	relaxes
volume of thorax	increases	decreases
pressure in thorax	decreases	increases
outside air (atmospheric) pressure	Greater, therefore air moves in	Less, therefore air moves out

> Complete the table to show how pressure changes are achieved in the thorax.

SYLLABUS CHECK
Control of breathing is required by the AQA(A), AQA(B) and Edexcel syllabuses.

LUNG CAPACITY

Terms are used to describe the different volumes of air held in the lungs.

Term	Volume (dm³)	
tidal volume	0.5	normal breathing
inspiratory reserve volume	2.0	deepest breath in (A)
expiratory reserve volume	1.5	deepest breath out (B)
vital capacity	3.5	volume between A and B
residual volume	1.5	lungs are never empty

> Complete the table, giving the appropriate term used to describe the volume of air exchanged.

DON'T FORGET
The pattern of change in lung volume during human breathing can be analysed using an instrument called a spirometer.

Turn the page for some exam questions on this topic ▶

AQA(A) AQA(B) EDEXCEL OCR WJEC

Blood is a type of connective tissue consisting of several types of cells suspended in a liquid matrix called plasma.

FUNCTIONS OF BLOOD

Blood carries out a number of functions.

Blood component	Function
plasma	transport of materials e.g. digested food, urea, CO_2, etc.
erythrocytes	transport of O_2 as oxyhaemoglobin
granulocytes	phagocytosis
lymphocytes	produce antibodies

Complete the table, listing the appropriate blood component.

SYLLABUS CHECK
Skip the transport of respiratory gases if you're studying the AQA(A) syllabus.

DON'T FORGET
Granulocytes and lymphocytes are different types of leucocytes.

TRANSPORT OF CO_2 – THE CHLORIDE SHIFT

In addition to its role in O_2 transport, haemoglobin also helps the blood transport CO_2, and assists in buffering the blood.

Reaction site	Reaction
RBC	CO_2 + water = carbonic acid
RBC	carbonic acid dissociates into H^+ and HCO_3^-
RBC/plasma	HCO_3^- diffuses out of RBC
plasma	NaCl dissociates into Na^+ and Cl^-
plasma	$HCO_3^- + Na^+$ = sodium hydrogen carbonate
RBC	H^+ encourages HbO_2 to dissociate to $Hb + O_2$
RBC	$H^+ + Hb = HHb$ O_2 diffuses out of RBC into tissues To balance outward movement of negative ions, chloride ions diffuse in.

THE JARGON
Buffering prevents harmful changes in pH.

The reaction steps in the table take place in either the red blood cells or the plasma. State the appropriate site in the boxes.

THE JARGON
RBC is an abbreviation for red blood cell.

DON'T FORGET
The majority of the carbon dioxide produced by the tissues combines with water to form carbonic acid. This reaction is catalysed by the enzyme carbonic anhydrase.

DON'T FORGET
The pH decreases (becomes more acidic) in very active tissues because the CO_2 produced by respiration reacts with water to form carbonic acid, which dissociates to give H^+ and HCO_3^-.

OXYGEN TRANSPORT – THE BOHR EFFECT

The release of oxygen from haemoglobin is aided by the presence of carbon dioxide. The graph shows the oxygen dissociation curve for haemoglobin.

pO_2 (mmHg)	% Saturation at pH 7.4	at pH 7.2	% O_2 released at pH 7.4	at pH 7.2
104 (in lungs)	98	---	---	---
40 (in tissues)	75	65	24	33
10 (muscle tissue)	18	10	80	88

Interpret the graph, then complete the table. Notice how more oxygen is released when the curve shifts to the right.

EXAMINER'S SECRETS
At pH 7.4 and at a pO_2 of 40 mm Hg, haemoglobin is only 75% saturated, i.e. it gives up 24% of its O_2 to the tissues (99 – 75 = 24)

Turn the page for some exam questions on this topic ▶

For more on this topic, see pages 36–37 of the Revision Express A-level Study Guide

EXAM QUESTION 1

The oxygen dissociation curve of human haemoglobin for a normal person at rest at 37°C and for a human fetus are shown in the graph.

If you are sure you understand the oxygen dissociation curve, have a go at this question.

(a) State the % saturation of adult blood with oxygen when pO_2 is:

4 kPa   *40%*

6 kPa   *80%*

(b) How would the dissociation curve differ if the blood had a high concentration of carbon dioxide?

It would be a similar shape but displaced to the right.

(c) What is the significance of this difference?

The displacement to the right means that haemoglobin (Hb) has a lower affinity for oxygen when CO_2 concentrations are high. Since such concentrations occur in respiring tissues, Hb readily gives up its O_2 at these tissues.

(d) What is the importance of the fetus having a haemoglobin that differs from that of the adult?

The fetal haemoglobin has a dissociation curve to the left of that of the adult and therefore has a greater affinity for O_2. It can absorb O_2 from the maternal haemoglobin in the placenta.

(e) Where would the dissociation curve for myoglobin be in relation to that for adult Hb? Give an explanation for your answer.

Myoglobin occurs in the muscles where it acts as a store of O_2. It also would have its curve displaced to the left. Its higher affinity for O_2 allows it to readily absorb O_2 from the Hb in the blood.

(f) Where would the dissociation curve for a llama be in relation to that of the adult human? Explain your answer.

A llama lives at high altitude, making it difficult to load Hb. Its curve would also be to the left.

THE JARGON
Oxygen concentration is measured by partial pressure, otherwise called the oxygen tension.
The units are kiloPascals or kPa.

B1 Blood vessels

There are three types of blood vessel. Arteries carry blood away from the heart, veins carry blood to the heart and the much smaller capillaries link arteries to veins.

EXAMINER'S SECRETS

It may at first seem that blood should travel faster through capillaries than through arteries, because the diameter of the capillaries is much smaller. However, it is the *total cross-sectional area* delivering the blood that determines flow rate. It is essential that the blood flow is slow in capillary beds to allow time for the transfer of materials between the blood and the tissue fluid.

STRUCTURE AND FUNCTION OF BLOOD VESSELS ○○○

Structural differences in the walls of the different blood vessels correlate with their different functions.

Arteries have thick muscular, elastic walls. They need strength and elasticity to accommodate changes in blood flow and pressure.

Veins have fewer elastic and muscular fibres in their walls. Blood flows in them back to the heart at low velocity and pressure. Skeletal muscles squeeze the veins and valves prevent backflow.

Capillaries possess a wall which is only one cell thick, allowing rapid exchange of materials by diffusion. Blood flow is slowed in them because their total cross-sectional area is much greater than in arteries.

Feature	Artery	Vein	Capillary
muscle layer	thick	thin	none
elastic layer	much	little	none
lumen (relative to diameter)	small	large	large
valves	no	yes	no
permeability	no	no	yes
blood pressure	high	low	reducing
blood flow	rapid	slow	slowing

THE JARGON

As blood passes from arterioles into the narrow capillaries, a hydrostatic pressure forces out fluid through the capillary walls. This fluid is called *tissue fluid* and bathes all the cells of the body. It contains glucose, amino acids, fatty acids and oxygen which it supplies to the tissues.

EXCHANGE OF MATERIALS BETWEEN CAPILLARIES AND TISSUE FLUID ○○○

The diagram shows the formation and destination of tissue fluid:

Complete the table by using the information provided in the text.

Draw arrows on the diagram to show:
- **the direction of blood flow**
- **the direction and destination of tissue fluid.**

Most tissue fluid passes into venules, some passes into lymph vessels (and is then known as lymph).

Exchange takes place in the capillary beds by pressure filtration:

Explain the forces involved in pressure filtration

Hydrostatic pressure forces fluid through the capillary walls and the reduced water potential, caused by blood plasma proteins, draws much of it back.

Turn the page for some exam questions on this topic ➤

For more on this topic, see pages 38–39 of the *Revision Express A-level Study Guide*

EXAM QUESTION 1

Diagrams A, B and C show cross sections of three different types of blood vessels. They are not drawn to the same scale.

Try this question which asks you to identify the blood vessels.

(a) Identify the blood vessels.

A artery   B vein   C capillary

(b) State two ways in which vessel C is adapted for its functions.

Thin wall and a relatively large lumen.

EXAM QUESTION 2

This question requires you to apply your knowledge.

The table shows the maximum and minimum blood pressures (in kPa) at various points in selected arteries and capillaries.

Site	Blood pressure (kPa)	
	Maximum	Minimum
pulmonary artery	3.33	1.07
muscle capillary	2.00	2.00
lung capillary	1.07	0.67

DON'T FORGET

The pulmonary artery carries blood from the lungs back to the heart.

(a) There is a difference between arterial pressures and the capillary pressures. Explain, in relation to the *functions* of these vessels, why this is more efficient.

- The function of arteries is transport, which is efficient at high speed, i.e. high pressure.
- Capillary function is exchange of materials. The reducing pressure slows blood flow, allowing more time for exchange.

(b) (i) Compare the values for capillaries in the muscle with capillaries in the lung.

The muscle capillaries have a more constant pressure than the lung capillaries where the pressure fluctuates.

(ii) Suggest why these differences occur.

- The left ventricle supplies blood to the muscles, the right ventricle supplies blood to lungs.
- The fluctuations in the pulmonary artery are due to respiratory movements and proximity to the heart. The blood moves slowly through the lung capillaries to allow time for diffusion of gases.
- Elastic tissue in aorta and great vessels smooths pressure into the muscles.

DON'T FORGET

The muscular wall of the left ventricle of the heart is about three times as thick as that of the right ventricle. This difference is related to the greater distance that blood is pumped by the left ventricle, and the resistance that it has to overcome in serving the whole body.

(c) Give one reason to explain how a return flow to the heart is possible when the vein pressures are so low.

- The relaxing heart has a suction effect.
- The massaging effect of muscles.
- The prevention of backflow by valves.

The heart

Each day the heart beats up to 100 000 times and pumps out 13 000 dm³ of blood.

THE CARDIAC CYCLE

The cardiac muscles of the heart contract and relax in a rhythmic cycle.

Fill in the missing words.

When the heart ...A... it pumps blood and when it ...B... its chambers fill with blood. One complete sequence of pumping and filling is called the ...C... cycle. A contraction phase of the cycle is called ...D... and a relaxation phase is called ...E.....

A *contracts*   B *relaxes*   C *cardiac*

D *systole*   E *diastole*

The myogenic stimulation of the heart is maintained by the transmission of a wave of electrical activity. Three groups of tissues are involved.

IF YOU HAVE TIME
Draw a section through the heart and from memory label the chambers, valves and associated blood vessels. Use a coloured pen to show the circulation of blood through the heart.

THE JARGON
The heart muscle is *myogenic*, that is, the heart beat is initiated from within the muscle itself and is not due to nervous stimulation.

A sinoatrial (SA) node   B atrioventricular node
C bundle of His   D left atrium
E left ventricle   F right ventricle
G right atrium

Label A to G on the diagram. Labels D to G are the chambers of the heart.

THE JARGON
Another term for atrium is auricle.

1. The impulses are delayed at the AV node for about 0.1 seconds, during which blood in the atria empties into the ventricles.
2. The ventricles contract simultaneously from the apex upwards.
3. Blood is driven into the large arteries.
4. The new wave of excitation from the AV node is conducted along Purkyne fibres which collectively make up the bundle of His.
5. The fibres conduct impulses to the apex of the heart and throughout the ventricular walls.
6. The SA node generates electrical impulses that spread through both atria, making them contract simultaneously.

Place steps 1 to 6 of the control of heartbeat (cardiac cycle) in the correct order.

6-1-4-5-2-3

THE JARGON
'Purkyne' is spelt 'Purkinje' in some textbooks.

FACTORS MODIFYING HEART RATE

The cardiac output can be calculated using an equation:

Cardiac output = heart rate (pulse) × stroke volume = 5.25 dm³/min

THE JARGON
Stroke volume is the amount of blood pumped by the left ventricle each time it contracts.

If the stroke volume is 75 millilitres and the heart rate is 70 beats per minute, use the equation to calculate the cardiac output per minute.

List two different body systems that can modify heart rate.

hormones and nerves

Turn the page for some exam questions on this topic ►

For more on this topic, see pages 40–41 of the *Revision Express A-level Study Guide*

EXAM QUESTION 1

This question asks about some general features of heart structure and function.

(a) State three essential features of a circulating mass flow system.

A transport medium (blood), a pump (the heart) and a drive control (valves), blood vessels.

(b) State an advantage of
   (i) a double circulation system

Pressure is restored after blood has passed through the lung capillaries.

   (ii) a four-chambered heart.

There is no mixing of oxygenated and deoxygenated blood so that delivery of oxygen to the body is enhanced.

(c) Describe and explain
   (i) the difference between the pressure of the blood leaving the left ventricle (LV) and the pressure of the blood leaving the right ventricle (RV).

The pressure is higher from the left. The LV has thicker and more powerful muscle to send the blood a greater distance all round the body.

   (ii) the relationship between the cardiac output of the left side of the heart and the cardiac output of the right side of the heart.

They are equal, otherwise blood would accumulate on one side.

EXAM QUESTION 2

The diagram shows a normal electrocardiogram (ECG) for one heartbeat.

This question requires you to have a good understanding of the control of the cardiac cycle.

P represents the electrical activity as it passes over the atria.

Q, R and S represent the spread of electrical activity over the ventricles. T indicates the electrical recovery of the ventricles.

THE JARGON
An electrocardiogram shows the pattern of electrical activity associated with a heart.

(a) Give the name of the tissue of the heart represented by the electrical activity at Q R S.

Purkyne fibres which make up the bundle of His.

(b) There is a delay of 0.1 seconds between P and Q. Explain what causes this delay and why it is important in the functioning of the heart.

Delay is caused by AV node, so that blood in the atria can enter the ventricles.

(c) What is happening to the blood in the heart during T?

The ventricles are being repolarized, allowing time for blood to enter the heart again.

Transport in plants

In plants the roots, which collect the water, are some distance from the leaves that require it for photosynthesis. A transport system of specialized cells connects the two structures.

STRUCTURE OF THE STEM

The diagram shows a transverse section (T.S.) through a typical dicotyledonous stem.

> **Label parts A to F in the diagram.**

A	cambium	B	fibres	C	phloem
D	xylem	E	cortex	F	epidermis

IF YOU HAVE TIME
Your practical work with the microscope should be studied in conjunction with this section. Draw xylem and phloem in transverse section (T.S.) and longitudinal section (L.S.) and be able to distinguish and identify cells in the two views.

LINKS
For more information on leaf structure, see page 45.

CHECK THE NET
You'll find information and exercises on plant cell types and organs at: wsuonline.weber.edu/course.botany.130/unit1_1a.htm

STRUCTURE OF THE ROOT

The diagram shows a T.S. through a root.

> **Label parts A to F in the diagram.**

A	epidermis	B	cortex	C	endodermis
D	phloem	E	xylem	F	root hair

STRUCTURE OF VASCULAR TISSUES

Xylem tissue consists of four different types of cells.

1. vessels   water transport and support
2. tracheids   support
3. fibres
4. xylem parenchyma

Phloem tissue also consists of four different types of cells.

1. sieve tube elements   transport of sucrose
2. companion cells   metabolism
3. phloem fibres
4. phloem parenchyma

> **List the cells which make up xylem and phloem and give the functions of the two main cells in each tissue.**

EXAMINER'S SECRETS
A thorough understanding of xylem and phloem cell structure is essential to enable you to answer questions on the mechanisms of transport in plants.

Turn the page for some exam questions on this topic ▶

For more on this topic, see page 42 of the *Revision Express A-level Study Guide*

EXAM QUESTION 1

Diagrams A and B represent T.S. stem and T.S. root, showing the distribution of the main tissue types.

> **Try this question which asks you to distinguish between the root and stem.**

(a) **Which diagram A, or B, is the T.S. stem? Give a reason for your answer.**

A • vascular bundles are to periphery
  • xylem and phloem are on same radius.

(B) **Write the name of the different tissues which carry out the functions below.**

transport of sugars   phloem
transport of water   xylem
cell division   cambium

EXAM QUESTION 2

The statements refer to specific cells found in xylem and phloem.

> **If the statement is correct place a tick in the appropriate box.**

Statement	Xylem vessels	Sieve tubes
provide support	✓	
walls contain lignin	✓	
transport in one direction	✓	
made up of cells joined end to end	✓	✓
possess living contents		✓

EXAM QUESTION 3

The diagrams show sections through the same tissue in a dicotyledonous stem.

(a) **Name the cell types labelled A to C on diagram I.**

A companion cell B sieve tube element C phloem parenchyma

(b) **Label equivalent cells A and B on diagram II.**

(c) **What is structure D?** sieve plate

© Pearson Education Limited 2001

For more on this topic; see pages 44–45 of the *Revision Express A-level Study Guide*

Transport of water through the plant

Water from the soil enters the plant through the epidermis of the root, crosses the root cortex, passes into the xylem of the vascular bundle and then flows up the xylem vessels to the shoot system and to the leaves.

WATER TRANSPORT ACROSS THE ROOT CORTEX

Once water enters the root, by a combination of soaking into the epidermal cells and osmosis, it travels across the cortex. The diagram shows the three routes for water transport across cells.

vacuole   cytoplasm   cell wall

Pathway	Cell structure
A apoplast	cell wall
B vacuolar	cell vacuoles
C symplast	cytoplasm via plasmodesmata

Complete the table to identify the three pathways of water transport through cells.

DON'T FORGET
A water potential gradient exists across the cortex. The WP is high in the root hair cells and lower in the adjacent cells.

THE JARGON
The Casparian strip is made of suberin which is a waxy material that is impervious to water and dissolved minerals.

THE ROLE OF THE ENDODERMIS

The endodermis blocks the apoplast pathway and regulates the ions which the plant draws into the xylem. The diagram shows two views of endodermal cells.

Casparian strip

direction in which water passes through endodermal cell

Water and minerals can only get past the barrier by being diverted into the ...A... pathway. Since the xylem lacks cell contents the entry of water and minerals into the xylem require their return to the ...B... pathway in the cells internal to the endodermis. Diffusion and ...C... are thought to be involved in the transfer of solutes.

A symplast   B apoplast   C active transport

IF YOU HAVE TIME
Make notes on the active uptake of mineral ions and their movement in the transpiration stream.

Explain the role of the endodermis as a selective sentry between the root cortex and the vascular tissue by filling in the blanks in the description.

THE COHESION–TENSION THEORY

Evaporation of water from the leaves provides the pull and the cohesion of water transmits the upward pull along the length of the xylem to the roots.

water loss from leaf drawing water from the xylem — transpiration pull

hydrogen bonding between water molecules — cohesion

forces between the water molecules and the walls of the xylem vessels — adhesion

List the forces which contribute to the movement of water up the stem.

Turn the page for some exam questions on this topic ▶

EXAM QUESTION 1

cell C   cell B   cell A   apoplast pathway

The diagram shows some root cells in a transverse section.

(a) Explain briefly, in terms of water potential, how water moves from the soil into cell A.
- Cell A has a lower (more negative) water potential than the soil solution.
- Water moves into the cell by osmosis.

(b) Draw a line on the diagram to show the apoplast pathway through these cells.

(c) Cell C is the innermost layer of cells of the cortex.

Give the name of this layer.

Endodermis.

This question is quite straightforward. It does not ask for much detail.

IF YOU HAVE TIME
Draw a diagram of a plant showing the roots, stem and leaves. On it show the pathway of water and indicate the active and passive processes which take place at the appropriate points.

EXAM QUESTION 2

Describe the route taken by water travelling from the soil to the leaf and the forces involved in this movement.

These factors might be mentioned in an ideal answer.

	force/process involved
materials move in solution with a combined push from below and pull from above	root pressure
active transport establishes an osmotic gradient across apoplast of cortex	active transport
removal of ions from apoplast of cortex into symplast (causing low concentration)	a high osmotic gradient is created
water moves through cells via plasmodesmata into stele	no force involved
leak from stele back into apoplast (causing high concentration)	cohesion resulting in 'pull'
bonding between water molecules	adhesion
bonding between water and hydrophilic walls of vessels	capillarity
very small diameter of vessels and tracheids	transpiration
evaporation of water from leaves	transpiration pull
replacement of water from below as a mass flow	

Try planning this essay question. It's quite tricky.

IF YOU HAVE TIME
Use the statements to write out your essay.

DON'T FORGET
Long distance transport of water from roots to leaves occurs by mass flow, the movement of water driven by a pressure difference at opposite ends of a continuous system of channels, formed by the vessels and tracheids.

Transpiration

About 99% of the water moving through the plant is lost from the leaves as water vapour. This evaporation of water through the stomata of the leaves is known as transpiration.

THE ROLE OF TRANSPIRATION

○○○

Water loss is a consequence of having pores in the leaf to allow the exchange of gases for photosynthesis. However, it also has useful functions in the plant.

- Maintains a water potential gradient from the roots to the leaves.
- A cooling effect by evaporation from a surface.
- The transfer of minerals from roots to leaves.

List three ways in which transpiration contributes to the functioning of the plant

DON'T FORGET
Some water is also lost through the cuticle.

FACTORS AFFECTING TRANSPIRATION RATE

○○○

Water vapour diffuses from a region of high WP to a region of low WP down a water potential gradient. The diagram shows this situation in a section of a typical leaf.

high WP

water vapour
low WP in atmospheric air

DON'T FORGET
The water potential of the atmosphere is determined by the interaction of these factors.

LINK
For more information on opening and closing of stomata, see page 45. This is the means by which the plant controls the WP gradient.

Any factor which alters the size of the gradient will influence the rate of transpiration.

Condition	Increase	Decrease
high humidity		✓
increase in light intensity	✓	
still air		✓
high temperature	✓	

Tick the boxes to indicate if there is an increase or decrease in transpiration under the conditions shown.

XEROPHYTES

○○○

Xerophytes have adapted to living under conditions of low water availability and so have modified structures to prevent excessive water loss:

Feature that minimizes water loss	Effect
thick leaf cuticle	reduces cuticular transpiration
layer of epidermal hairs	traps moist air and reduces WP gradient
sunken stomata	moist air trapped outside stomata, reducing WP gradient
rolled leaf	ratio of external surface to volume is small with moist internal atmosphere

Describe the specific effect of the modification (where possible in terms of how it affects the WP gradient).

SYLLABUS CHECK
Skip xerophytes if you're studying the Edexcel syllabus.
The WJEC syllabus requires you to study a specific example, marram grass.

Turn the page for some exam questions on this topic ▶

For more on this topic, see page 43 of the *Revision Express A-level Study Guide*

EXAM QUESTION 1

Graphs A, B and C give the effect of three external conditions on the rate of transpiration in plants.

Have a go at this question concerning factors that affect the rate of transpiration.

Describe how each factor influences the rate of transpiration.

Graph A   The transpiration rate will increase as the moisture content of the atmosphere falls since the WP gradient increases.

Graph B   A rise in temperature lowers the relative humidity of the air so that it can hold more water (it also increases the kinetic energy of water molecules and so increases rate of evaporation). The rate of transpiration increases.

Graph C   Wind blows away water-laden air outside the stomata and the WP gradient increases.

DON'T FORGET
You should describe the effect in terms of water potential gradient.

EXAM QUESTION 2

The 'Two-leaf Hakea' is a plant found in south-west Australia, where the spring is relatively cool and wet but the summer is very hot and dry. The plant produces one type of leaf in spring (A) and a different type (B) in the summer. The table shows the average values of a range of measurements taken from the leaves.

This question is about how a xerophyte is adapted to cope with periods of water stress.

Characteristic of leaf	A	B
length (mm)	33	55
maximum width (mm)	10	0.8
surface area (mm²)	292	144
volume (mm³)	64	63
cuticle thickness (µm)	14	24

(a) Calculate the surface area (SA) to volume ratio for leaves A and B.

A   4.6 : 1   B   2.3 : 1

(b) Use the data in the table to list four ways in which leaf type B is adapted to summer conditions in south-west Australia.

thick cuticle   needle leaves   reduced SA/volume ratio   smaller SA so a reduced number of stomata

(c) Suggest and explain one advantage to the plant of producing leaf type A in the spring.

More water is available, so a larger leaf SA is needed to absorb additional light for photosynthesis.

For more on this topic, see pages 46–47 of the *Revision Express A-level Study Guide*

Translocation

AQA(B) EDEXCEL OCR WJEC

There is considerable controversy regarding the mechanism by which materials are translocated in phloem. However, it is agreed that the observed rate of flow is much too fast for diffusion to be the cause.

MECHANISM OF TRANSLOCATION

The diagram shows a model which is used to explain how organic substances move through a plant. A and B represent cells surrounded by membranes permeable only to water.

Complete the diagram by adding arrow heads to the lines in the diagram to show the direction in which fluid will move (at A, B, C and D).

LINK
For more information on the structure of phloem, see page 55.

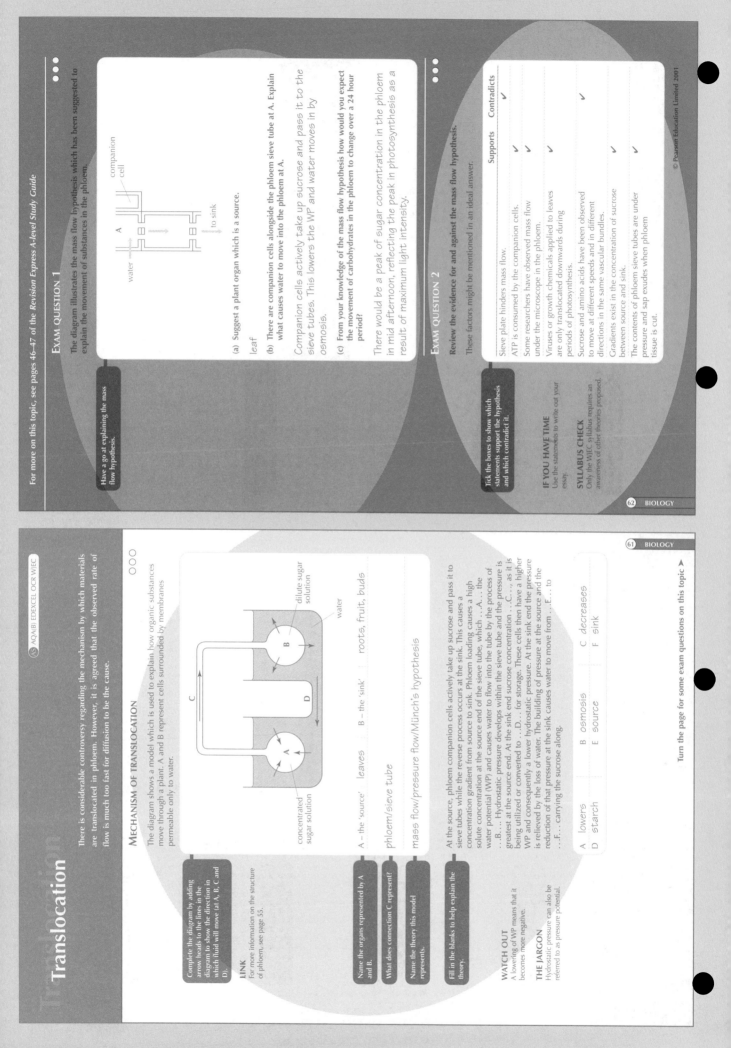

concentrated sugar solution

dilute sugar solution

water

Name the organs represented by A and B.

A – the 'source'   leaves   B – the 'sink'   roots, fruit, buds

What does connection C represent?

phloem/sieve tube

Name the theory this model represents.

mass flow/pressure flow/Munch's hypothesis

At the source, phloem companion cells actively take up sucrose and pass it to sieve tubes while the reverse process occurs at the sink. This causes a concentration gradient from source to sink. Phloem loading causes a high solute concentration at the source end of the sieve tube, which ...A... the water potential (WP) and causes water to flow into the tube by the process of ...B... Hydrostatic pressure develops within the sieve tube and the pressure is greatest at the source end. At the sink end sucrose concentration ...C..., as it is being utilized or converted to ...D... for storage. These cells then have a higher WP and consequently a lower hydrostatic pressure. At the sink end the pressure is relieved by the loss of water. The building of pressure at the source and the reduction of that pressure at the sink causes water to move from ...E... to ...F... carrying the sucrose along.

Fill in the blanks to help explain the theory.

A lowers   B osmosis   C decreases
D starch   E source   F sink

WATCH OUT
A lowering of WP means that it becomes more negative.

THE JARGON
Hydrostatic pressure can also be referred to as pressure potential.

Turn the page for some exam questions on this topic ▶

EXAM QUESTION 1

Have a go at explaining the mass flow hypothesis.

The diagram illustrates the mass flow hypothesis which has been suggested to explain the movement of substances in the phloem.

water — A — to sink — companion cell

(a) Suggest a plant organ which is a source.

leaf

(b) There are companion cells alongside the phloem sieve tube at A. Explain what causes water to move into the phloem at A.

Companion cells actively take up sucrose and pass it to the sieve tubes. This lowers the WP and water moves in by osmosis.

(c) From your knowledge of the mass flow hypothesis how would you expect the movement of carbohydrates in the phloem to change over a 24 hour period?

There would be a peak of sugar concentration in the phloem in mid afternoon, reflecting the peak in photosynthesis as a result of maximum light intensity.

EXAM QUESTION 2

Review the evidence for and against the mass flow hypothesis.

These factors might be mentioned in an ideal answer.

Tick the boxes to show which statements support the hypothesis and which contradict it.

	Supports	Contradicts
Sieve plate hinders mass flow.		✓
ATP is consumed by the companion cells.	✓	
Some researchers have observed mass flow under the microscope in the phloem.	✓	
Viruses or growth chemicals applied to leaves are only translocated downwards during periods of photosynthesis.	✓	
Sucrose and amino acids have been observed to move at different speeds and in different directions in the same vascular bundles.		✓
Gradients exist in the concentration of sucrose between source and sink.	✓	
The contents of phloem sieve tubes are under pressure and sap exudes when phloem tissue is cut.	✓	

IF YOU HAVE TIME
Use the statements to write out your essay.

SYLLABUS CHECK
Only the WJEC syllabus requires an awareness of other theories proposed.

For more on this topic, see pages 54–55 of the *Revision Express A-level Study Guide*

Ecosystems and energy

Energy enters an ecosystem, flows within it, and eventually exits from it.

THE ECOSYSTEM

Give the correct term for each definition.

The following are the definitions of some terms used in the study of ecosystems.

Definition	Term
A group of individuals of one species occupying a particular area.	population
A particular area occupied by a population.	habitat
All the organisms that inhabit a particular area.	community
All the organisms living in a community as well as all the abiotic factors with which they interact.	ecosystem
The feeding level in a food chain.	trophic level

PRIMARY PRODUCTIVITY

As little as 1% of the sun's radiant light energy is converted to chemical energy by plants for distribution throughout the ecosystem, but this is sufficient to support all life on Earth.

Complete the equation.

net primary productivity (NPP) = $\dfrac{\text{gross primary productivity (GPP)} - \text{respiration}}{}$

DON'T FORGET
NPP represents the storage of chemical energy to consumers in an ecosystem.

WATCH OUT
Don't confuse NPP with the total biomass of autotrophs present at a given time, called the standing crop biomass. Primary productivity is the rate at which the organism synthesizes new biomass.

THE JARGON
Trophic efficiency is the percentage of energy at one trophic level which is incorporated into the next trophic level.

TROPHIC EFFICIENCY AND ENERGY LOSS

In the secondary consumer illustrated more than half the food eaten passes straight through (figures show the energy flow in kJ/m²/y⁻¹).

Use the information in the diagram to answer the question.

3060 kJ eaten → **COW**

- 1020 kJ respiration
- 125 kJ to growth (secondary production)
- 3520 kJ eaten by other herbivores
- 1910 kJ faeces and urine (excretion)
- 14860 kJ to decomposers

Calculate % excreted
(3060 − 1910 = 1150 is absorbed into the blood)
1910/3060 × 100 = 62.42%

Calculate % respired
1020/1150 × 100 = 88.70%

Calculate % in growth
125/1150 × 100 = 10.87%

So only about 10% of the absorbed energy is available to the next trophic level. How much energy is consumed by other organisms?
14 860 + 3520 = 18 380 kJ

Why does a cow seem to eat all day long, whereas a lion eats about once a week?
A protein rich diet is more readily and efficiently digested. Only about 20% of energy intake of carnivores is lost in excretion.

Turn the page for some exam questions on this topic ▶

EXAM QUESTION 1

Have a go at answering a question about a sheep this time!

The diagram shows what happens to food energy consumed by a sheep (all units are MJ/day⁻¹).

sheep
- consumption 28.5
- respiration 10.2
- production
- faeces and urine 13.0

(a) Which group of organisms use faeces of herbivores as an energy source?
decomposers

(b) Calculate, showing your working.
(i) The amount of energy that goes into the production of new tissue by the sheep.
28.5 − (13.0 + 10.2) = 5.3 MJ/day⁻¹

(ii) The efficiency with which energy in plant food is transferred to energy in new tissue in the sheep.
5.3/28.5 = 19%

(c) Intensive farming involves keeping animals inside and feeding them as required. Suggest and explain one way in which intensive farming can improve the efficiency of energy transfer.
Restricting movement and reducing heat loss. This results in less energy loss in respiration.

EXAM QUESTION 2

This question is about an ecosystem.

The table shows the flow of energy in a tropical forest.

Trophic level	Energy entering (kJ/m²/y⁻¹)
producers	200×10^3
primary consumers	6.7×10^3
secondary consumers	6.7×10^2
tertiary consumers	6.7×10^1
decomposers	23.6×10^3

(a) (i) If the producers lose 133×10^3 kJ/m²/y⁻¹ through respiration, what percentage of their stored energy is taken up by primary consumers?
$(200 - 135) \times 10^3 = 67 \times 10^3$
$\text{\% stored energy} = \dfrac{6.7 \times 10^3 \times 100}{67 \times 10^3}$
$= 10\%$

(ii) Explain why the energy entering the decomposers is greater than that entering all the consumers.
Decomposers receive energy from all trophic levels including producers.

(b) Predict one way in which the data for the tropical forest might differ from a forest ecosystem in Britain.
Less energy entering producers (less sunshine).

Food chains and food webs

EDEXCEL OCR WJEC

Each ecosystem has a trophic structure of feeding relationships. Ecologists divide the organisms in a community or ecosystem into trophic levels on the basis of their main source of nutrition.

TROPHIC LEVELS AND FEEDING RELATIONSHIPS

These are some definitions of terms used in connection with feeding relationships.

Definition	Term
The pathway along which food is transferred from trophic level to trophic level, beginning with the primary producers.	food chain
The elaborate, interconnected feeding relationships in an ecosystem.	food web
An organism that uses energy from the sun to make organic molecules from inorganic.	autotroph
An organism that obtains organic food molecules by eating other organisms or their by-products.	heterotroph
An organism that acts as a decomposer by absorbing nutrients from dead organic matter.	saprobiont
An organism that obtains nutrients from the body fluids of living hosts.	parasite
An organism which feeds on small fragments of organic debris from decomposing plants and animals.	detritivore
Microbes that obtain nutrients from dead organisms, faeces etc. by extracellular digestion.	decomposers

Give the correct term for the definitions.

LINKS
An ecosystem's trophic structure determines the route of energy flow and nutrient cycling. See pages 61 and 67.

DON'T FORGET
Natural feeding relationships are usually more like webs because some consumers feed at several different trophic levels.
Some autotrophs can also make organic molecules from the oxidation of inorganic molecules.

SYLLABUS CHECK
Some additional terms may be used in your syllabus.

IF YOU HAVE TIME
Make a list of all the organisms living in a habitat. Build up a food web by interconnecting all the organisms using arrows. Don't forget that the arrow heads indicate the direction of energy flow.

Organisms in a habitat occupy a particular trophic level.

grass	producer
caterpillar	primary consumer
toad	secondary consumer
snake	tertiary consumer
stoat	quaternary consumer
fungus	decomposer

THE JARGON
For the grassland habitat place the following organisms in the correct trophic level: fungus, toad, stoat, snake, caterpillar, grass.

THE JARGON
Detritus is made up of non-living organic material, such as faeces, fallen leaves and the remains of dead organisms.

DECOMPOSERS AND DETRITIVORES

Decomposition interconnects all trophic levels.

	A Detritivore	B Decomposer
size	larger	microscopic
type of digestion	internal	external
example	earthworm	bacteria
food	small fragments of organic debris	faeces

Insert the correct heading, decomposer or detritivore, at points A and B of the table.

DON'T FORGET
Decomposition accounts for most of the conversion of organic material from all trophic levels into inorganic compounds that are recycled.

Turn the page for some exam questions on this topic ➤

For more on this topic, see pages 56–57 of the *Revision Express A-level Study Guide*

EXAM QUESTION 1

The food web shows some of the feeding relationships of the peregrine falcon, a bird of prey which lives and nests on cliffs by the sea and feeds on other birds.

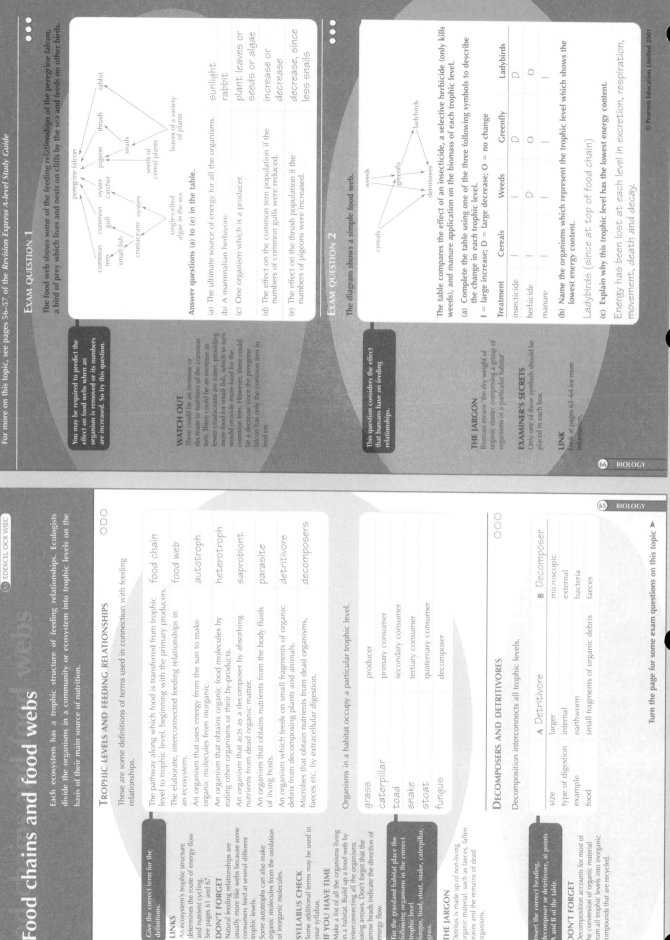

You may be required to predict the effect on food webs when an organism is removed or its numbers are increased. So try this question.

Answer questions (a) to (e) in the table.

Question	Answer
(a) The ultimate source of energy for all the organisms.	sunlight
(b) A mammalian herbivore.	rabbit
(c) One organism which is a producer.	plant leaves or seeds or algae
(d) The effect on the common tern population if the numbers of common gulls were reduced.	increase or decrease
(e) The effect on the thrush population if the numbers of pigeons were increased.	decrease, since less snails

WATCH OUT
There could be an increase or decrease in numbers of the common tern. There could be an increase as fewer crustaceans are eaten, providing more food for small fish, which in turn would provide more food for the common tern. However, there could be a decrease since the peregrine falcon has only the common tern to feed on.

EXAM QUESTION 2

The diagram shows a simple food web.

This question considers the effect that humans have on feeding relationships.

The table compares the effect of an insecticide, a selective herbicide (only kills weeds), and manure application on the biomass of each trophic level.

(a) Complete the table using one of the three following symbols to describe the change in each trophic level.

I = large increase; D = large decrease; O = no change

Treatment	Cereals	Weeds	Greenfly	Ladybirds
insecticide	I	I	D	D
herbicide	I	D	D	O
manure	I	I	I	I

(b) Name the organisms which represent the trophic level which shows the lowest energy content.

Ladybirds (since at top of food chain)

(c) Explain why this trophic level has the lowest energy content.

Energy has been lost at each level in excretion, respiration, movement, death and decay.

THE JARGON
Biomass means 'the dry weight of organic matter comprising a group of organisms in a particular habitat'.

EXAMINER'S SECRETS
Only one of these symbols should be placed in each box.

LINK
Look at pages 63–64 for more information.

Ecological pyramids

Within a community the food relationships and trophic levels can be shown by one or more ecological pyramids, as well as by food webs. The quantification of feeding relationships within a specific ecosystem involves obtaining numerical data.

THE THREE TYPES OF PYRAMIDS

The simplified diagrams show the three different ecological pyramids.

Identify pyramids A, B and C.

CHECK THE NET
You'll find information on ecological pyramids at:
www.sturgeon.ab.ca/rw/Pyramids/ecopyra.html

person
cows
grass
1
3
thousands

Numbers of each organism in a large field at a particular time

A

person
cows
grass
0.1
0.6
470

The dry mass (g/m²) of each group of organisms in the field

B

second level consumers
first level consumers
producer
90
1600
14 100

(units are kJ/m²/y⁻¹)

C

A Numbers   B Biomass   C Energy

THE DISADVANTAGES OF THE DIFFERENT PYRAMIDS

There are disadvantages in using the different forms of pyramids.

Describe the disadvantages of the different types of pyramids by putting the number of the statement which applies alongside the appropriate pyramid definition in the table below. (Some statements may be used more than once.)

1. It is difficult and laborious to obtain data.
2. Numbers of some individuals are so large it is impossible to represent them to scale.
3. Inverted pyramids can be created.
4. Organisms have to have their dry weight measured and this means destroying them.
5. All organisms are given the same value regardless of size.
6. No account is made for juvenile forms of a species whose diet and energy requirements may differ from the adult.
7. It is a snapshot view. This is called 'standing crop'.
8. Timing of taking the sample may affect the result and there is no indication of total productivity.
9. To measure the individuals a sample has to be taken and this may not be representative.
10. It is complex and difficult to obtain data.

THE JARGON
Standing crop describes the amount of living material present at a given instant in time.
The energy pyramid introduces a time factor and represents energy flow per unit time (say, one year). It therefore gives the best overall view of the community.
Units are kJ/m²/y⁻¹.

A pyramid of numbers is a bar diagram indicating the relative numbers of organisms at each trophic level in a food chain at any one time.	1, 2, 3, 5, 6, 7
A pyramid of biomass represents the total dry mass of organisms at each trophic level of a food chain at any one time.	1, 3, 4, 7, 8, 9
A pyramid of energy is a bar diagram drawn in proportion to the total energy utilized at each trophic level.	9, 10

Turn the page for some exam questions on this topic ▶

For more on this topic, see pages 58–59 of the *Revision Express A-level Study Guide*

EXAM QUESTION 1

A gardener was spraying a rose bush to try to get rid of the numerous greenfly which were feeding on the leaves and buds. He was helped by a few ladybirds. When he returned to his greenhouse he saw a blue tit eating some of the ladybirds.

Read the situation carefully before answering the question.

A   **B**   **C**

(a) Which one of the pyramids of numbers, A, B or C best represents the food chain described above?

Pyramid C

(b) Which shape would you expect for a pyramid of biomass for the same food chain?

Pyramid shape as in A above.

EXAM QUESTION 2

The diagram shows the pyramids of numbers and biomass in the same ecosystem.

Adapt some of the information on the previous page to answer this question.

15
100
1.5 × 10²
7 × 10¹⁰

Number of organisms (per m²)

1.5
10
40
800

Biomass (g/m⁻¹)

(a) **What are the advantages and disadvantages of the two methods of measurement?**

Pyramids of numbers are easier to measure but do not take account of size or juvenile forms. It may also be impossible to draw them to scale.

Pyramids of biomass are difficult to measure accurately. They measure only the 'standing crop' and give no indication of total productivity.

Both types can give inverted pyramids.

(b) **Explain why some aquatic ecosystems have inverted biomass pyramids, with primary consumers outweighing producers.**

Phytoplankton have a short 'turnover time'. They grow and reproduce rapidly but are consumed extremely rapidly by zooplankton.

THE JARGON
A short turnover time means a low standing crop biomass compared to the productivity.

(c) **What other type of pyramid could provide further information about the four trophic levels?**

pyramid of energy

Recycling of nutrients

Although ecosystems receive an inexhaustible influx of solar energy, chemical elements are available only in limited amounts. Life therefore depends on the recycling of essential chemical elements.

CHECK YOUR SYLLABUS
Leave out the carbon cycle if you're studying the OCR syllabus.

DON'T FORGET
The amount of carbon dioxide in the atmosphere varies slightly with the seasons and superimposed on this seasonal fluctuation is a continuing increase in the overall concentration of atmospheric CO_2 caused by the combustion of fossil fuels by humans.

WATCH OUT
Plants respire all the time just as animals do! During high light intensity the rate of photosynthesis is greater than the rate of respiration so the overall gas released is oxygen.

THE CARBON CYCLE
There is a balance between the removal of carbon dioxide from the air by the photosynthetic activity of green plants and its return as a result of the respiration of all organisms. The diagram shows a simplified version of the carbon cycle.

Insert the appropriate word from this list to describe the processes at work in A to D: decomposition, respiration, combustion, photosynthesis.

A respiration   B photosynthesis
C decomposition   D combustion

IF YOU HAVE TIME
If you're studying the WJEC syllabus write an account of the ways in which human activities affect the carbon and nitrogen cycles. These include eutrophication, the greenhouse effect and global warming. If you're studying the OCR syllabus confine your account to the nitrogen cycle.

Use the correct term that describes the microbial processes taking place in the nitrogen cycle.

THE NITROGEN CYCLE
The following statements describe decay processes at work in the nitrogen cycle.

Process	Term	Microbe
the conversion of inorganic nitrogen into ammonia	putrefaction/ ammonification	aerobic bacteria and fungi
the conversion of ammonia into nitrites and then nitrates	nitrification	Nitrosomonas Nitrobacter (aerobic)
the conversion of atmospheric nitrogen into nitrogen compounds	nitrogen fixation	Rhizobium (symbiotic) Azotobacter (free-living)
the reduction of nitrates to molecular nitrogen	denitrification	Pseudomonas Thiobacillus (anaerobic)

DON'T FORGET
Nitrogen is found in all amino acids which make up proteins. Nitrogen is available to plants only in the form of ammonium (NH_4^+) and nitrate (NO_3^-) ions which are taken up by the roots.

SYLLABUS CHECK
WJEC do not require the specific names of microbes. OCR require the specific names of Nitrosomonas, Nitrobacter and Rhizobium only. Edexcel require all the specific names listed in the table.

Explain why farming practices such as ploughing and improving drainage help improve soils.

Denitrification removes nitrogen from ecosystems. The activities aerate the soil so that anaerobic bacteria cannot compete with aerobic microbes and nitrates are not broken down to molecular nitrogen.

Turn the page for some exam questions on this topic ▶

For more on this topic, see pages 60–61 of the *Revision Express A-level Study Guide*

EXAM QUESTION 1

Try a multiple choice question.

Indicate the one correct answer by writing the letter A, B, C, or D below.

The process which is common to both the carbon and nitrogen cycle is:

A. combustion
B. decomposition   B
C. respiration
D. photosynthesis

EXAM QUESTION 2

This is a more demanding question on the nitrogen cycle.

The diagram represents the nitrogen cycle.

CHECK THE NET
You'll find information on how human activity is affecting nitrogen cycling at:
esa.sdsc.edu/tilman.htm
also at:
library.advanced.org/11353/text/nitrogen.htm

(a) What is the descriptive term applied to organisms at A and D?

A   nitrogen fixing bacteria
D   nitrifying bacteria

(b) Name processes B and H.

B   excretion   H   feeding

(c) Name the chemicals C, E and F.

C   ammonia   E   nitrites
F   nitrates

(d) Explain how growing leguminous plants such as clover, beans and peas at point A in a crop rotation scheme, could be used as a means of improving soil fertility.

Some nitrogen fixing bacteria (Rhizobium) live in symbiotic association with leguminous plants. They live in special swollen areas on roots called root nodules. The crop fixes nitrogen during its growth and may later be ploughed into the soil so that its decay can slowly release nitrogen compounds for use by later crops.

(e) What could be produced by human means at point G?
The chemical fixation of nitrogen to produce artificial nitrogenous fertilizers.

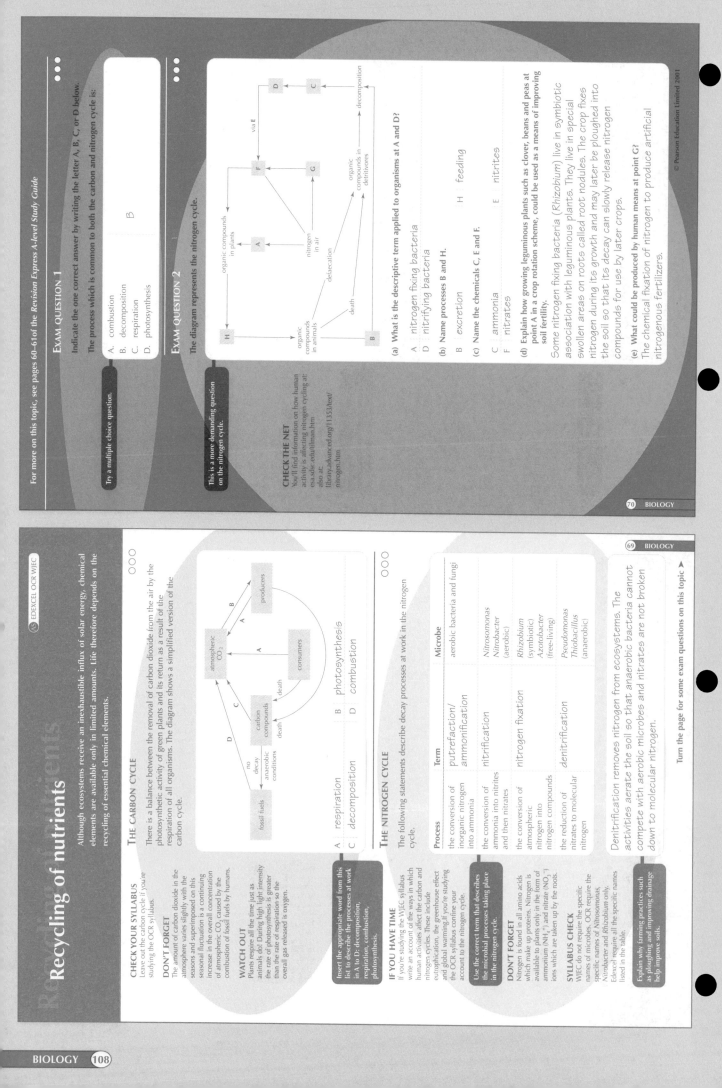

Resource management and human influences

AQA(A) EDEXCEL OCR WJEC

Humans are dependent on the Earth's resources for their survival. The increase in human population has meant that more food has to be produced to support it. In agriculture increased land use and the use of pesticides and fertilizers have improved crop yield. Environmental issues arise from their use.

RESOURCES

Renewable resources can be replaced whereas non-renewable resources cannot.

	Wood	Coal	Oil	Fish
renewable	✓			✓
non-renewable		✓	✓	

Tick the boxes to show whether the resources are renewable or not.

MANAGEMENT

The list describes some of the ways of counteracting poor environmental management.

insecticide resistance	biological control
deforestation	forest management
overfishing	quotas/net size/exclusion zone
fossil fuel pollution	nuclear/wind
eutrophication	reduce fertilizer application/reduce sewage into rivers

Suggest alternative resource management methods which may reduce the harmful effects.

IF YOU HAVE TIME
This section needs careful consideration. Check your own specification and devise your own revision cards.

THE JARGON
Lakes and rivers which suffer from eutrophication have little oxygen in the water.

HUMAN INFLUENCES

Humans can change the environment of crop plants.

using commercial glasshouses	Rate of photosynthesis increased by optimizing light intensity, temperature and carbon dioxide concentration.
applying insecticides	Insects damage crops and reduce photosynthetic area.
applying herbicides	Removal of weeds reduces competition between species.
adding fertilizer	Harvesting crops removes minerals from the soil. Mineral salts are needed for growth and have to be replenished.

Describe how these human activities can increase the yield of crops.

WATCH OUT
Don't simply state that yield is increased. Explain why.

Turn the page for some exam questions on this topic ➤

Human reproduction

The control of the menstrual cycle is an excellent example of hormonal interaction.

THE JARGON
Primary oocytes are in the diploid state and each month after puberty one of these cells completes its development into an ovum (egg).

SYLLABUS CHECK
The Edexcel syllabus requires a knowledge of additional sub-topics.

LINK
For more information on meiotic cell division, see page 29.

THE OVARY AND OOGENESIS

The ovary consists of a number of oocytes at various stages of development. The diagram shows the various stages observed in an idealized section through a human ovary.

Name the stages labelled A, B and C and explain why B changes in appearance to become D.

A Graafian follicle   B corpus luteum   C primary follicle
The ovum has not been fertilized/no pregnancy.

IF YOU HAVE TIME
If you're studying the AQA(A) syllabus make a list of the ways in which reproduction can be manipulated and controlled in humans and domestic animals.

HORMONAL CONTROL OF THE MENSTRUAL CYCLE

There are four hormones involved in the control of the female cycle and they are produced in a particular sequence.

Hormone	Gonadotrophic (pituitary)	Ovary	Order of production
oestrogen		✓	2
FSH	✓		1
progesterone		✓	4
LH	✓		3

Tick the boxes to show the site of production of the hormones and show the order of their production by placing numbers 1 to 4 in the appropriate column.

DON'T FORGET
All four hormones are always present at some level but their levels fluctuate.

The hormones have specific functions.

FSH	Causes Graafian follicles to develop in ovary. Stimulates ovary to produce oestrogen.
oestrogen	Inhibits the production and release of FSH. Causes regrowth of the uterus lining. Stimulates pituitary to produce LH.
LH	Brings about ovulation. Stimulates ovary to produce oestrogen and progesterone from the corpus luteum.
progesterone	Causes uterus lining to be maintained. Inhibits production of LH and FSH and stops further follicle development.

DON'T FORGET
The control of the menstrual cycle is an excellent example of hormone interaction, with an alternate switching on and off of the hormones. LH and FSH stimulate the ovaries to produce progesterone and oestrogen respectively.

Give the names of the hormones that carry out the functions listed.

WATCH OUT
This is a tricky topic. The study of graphs of the menstrual cycle will help your understanding.

Turn the page for some exam questions on this topic ▶

For more on this topic, see pages 134–139 of the *Revision Express A-level Study Guide*

EXAM QUESTION 1

Fill in the missing words in the gaps in the following passage.

A high level of oestrogen indirectly stimulates ovulation in female mammals by causing the release of two hormones, ...A... and ...B... The ...C... oocyte is released by the bursting of the ...D... After release, the structure which remains in the ovary forms a solid mass called the ...E... This structure secretes sufficient of the hormone ...F... to inhibit the production of ...G... by the ...H... gland. If fertilization occurs, it normally takes place in the ...I... The fertilized zygote undergoes repeated division to form a hollow ball of cells called a ...J... and after 3–5 days ...K... occurs in the uterine endometrium.

A LH	B FSH
C secondary	D Graafian follicle
E corpus luteum	F progesterone
G FSH	H anterior pituitary
I fallopian tube/oviduct	J blastocyst
K implantation	

Read the passage carefully before filling in the missing words.

EXAM QUESTION 2

The diagram shows phases in the average menstrual cycle of 28 days. Indicate by writing the appropriate letter, the phase in which you would expect each of the following events:

maximum secretion of LH	C
menstruation	A
fertilization	C
implantation of the fertilized egg	D

Place the appropriate letters in the boxes.

EXAM QUESTION 3

Complete the table to show the correct function(s) of luteinizing hormone (LH), oestrogen and progesterone.

Function	LH	Oestrogen	Progesterone
immediate cause of ovulation	✓		
immediate cause of regrowth of the uterine lining after menstruation		✓	
inhibits production of FSH		✓	✓
maintains the uterus for implantation			✓
stimulates the formation of a structure which produces progesterone	✓		

Tick the box or boxes to give the functions of the hormones. Take care, some hormones may have more than one function.

Index

Note: The page numbers in the index refer to the question section of the book. However, you may need to check the relevant answer pages for full information on a topic.